THE ARSENAL FC QUIZ BOOK

600 FUN QUESTIONS FOR ARSENAL FANS EVERYWHERE

JAMES CONRAD

INTRODUCTION

I take pride in the fact that people go home having felt for 90 minutes today, life is beautiful – and that's it, basically.
                                                            Arsene Wenger

This book has six hundred questions for dedicated Arsenal fans wherever you are. The questions are about its history, its achievements, its players, its managers and many other things.

The questions are generally in a multiple-choice format and are of varying degrees of difficulty to test the knowledge of all fans.

The Arsenal FC Quiz Book is both entertaining and informative and will provide hours of memory wracking entertainment for Arsenal fans.

CONTENTS

QUIZ 1: THE START

1. **What year was Arsenal founded?**
a) 1882   b) 1886   c) 1888

2. **What was the first name of the club?**
a) Woolwich Arsenal   b) The Gunners   c) Dial Square

3. **Which other football league club donated some old shirts for the players to wear which gave Arsenal their red and white colour shirts they wear today?**
a) Brentford   b) Nottingham Forest   c) Barnsley

4. **In what year were Woolwich Arsenal invited to join the football league?**
a) 1893   b) 1896   c) 1899

5. **In 1910 the club was close to going into liquidation. Which fellow London club's chairman led a business consortium to save the club?**
a) Fulham   b) Chelsea   c) Leyton Orient

6. **In 1919 the football league voted to promote Arsenal instead of which other club?**
a) Grimsby Town   b) Tottenham Hotspur   c) Leeds United

7. **What was Arsenal's first national trophy?**
a) FA Cup   b) First Division Trophy   c) Second Division Trophy

8. **Where did they finish in the league in their first season?**
a) Second   b) Sixth   c) Ninth

9. **When did Arsenal move to Highbury?**
a) 1901   b) 1907   c) 1913

10. **When was the last time Arsenal were relegated from the top division?**

   a) 1913   b) 1957   c) 1979

QUIZ 2: ARSENE WENGER

1. **What are Arsene Wenger's middle names?**

   a)   Louis Paul   b) Jacques Luc   c) Charles Ernest

2. **Which French club was his last as a player?**

   a)   Strasbourg b) Monaco c) Lyon

3. **Before joining Arsenal what country was Arsene managing in?**

   a)   Japan   b) France   c) Germany

4. **What year was he appointed manager of Arsenal?**

   a)   1995   b) 1996   c) 1997

5. **How many times did Arsenal win the FA Cup under Wenger?**

   a)   5   b) 6   c) 7

6. **Who was the full-time manager, not caretaker, of Arsenal prior to Wenger's arrival?**

   a)   George Graham   b) Terry Neil   c) Bruce Rioch

7. **Who were the first league opponents that Wenger faced as Arsenal manager?**

   a)   Blackburn Rovers   b) Liverpool   c) Norwich City

8. **How many trophies did Wenger win while at Arsenal?**

   a)   13   b) 15   c) 17

9. **What year did Wenger retire as manager of Arsenal?**

   a)   2016   b) 2017   c) 2018

10. **What was the score in Wenger's last match as manager of Arsenal against Huddersfield Town away?**

   a)   0-3   b) 2-2   c) 0-1

QUIZ 3: GEORGE GRAHAM

1. **What year was Graham born in?**
   a) 1940 b) 1944 c) 1948

2. **What club did Gorge join after leaving Arsenal as a player, during which time they were relegated to Division 2?**
   a) Manchester United b) Portsmouth c) Aston Villa

3. **How much did Arsenal pay for Graham in 1966?**
   a) £10,000 b) £30,000 c) £50,000

4. **At the end of his career Graham played for a team in which country?**
   a) Spain b) Italy c) USA

5. **How many times did he play for Scotland?**
   a) 1 b) 12 c) 28

6. **Which year did George take over as Arsenal manager?**
   a) 1982 b) 1984 c) 1986

7. **Which team was George's first managerial position?**
   a) Millwall b) Leeds United c) Arsenal

8. **Where did Arsenal finish in his first season in charge?**
   a) 4th b) 7th c) 10th

9. **In the 1992-93 Premier League season Arsenal scored the fewest goals in the league, how many did they score?**
   a) 35 b) 40 c) 45

10. **What was the reason George was sacked by Arsenal in 1995?**
    a) Poor form b) Fall out with director c) An unsolicited gift

QUIZ 4: TERRY NEILL

1. Which nationality was Neil?

a) Welsh   b) Scottish   c) Northern Irish

2. How old was Terry when he first became a manager?

a) 28   b) 30   c) 32

3. What was the first team he managed?

a) Hull City   b) Arsenal   c) Lincoln City

4. What was Terry Neill's first name?

a) John   b) William   c) Bob

5. Which club did Terry manage before taking over at Arsenal in 1976?

a) Chelsea   b) Manchester City   c) Tottenham Hotspur

6. Who did he take over from at Arsenal?

a) Bertie Mee   b) Billy Wright   c) Don Howe

7. In what season did Terry win the FA Cup, his only trophy with Arsenal?

a) 1976/77   b) 1978/79   c) 1980/81

8. In 1980 Arsenal reached the European Cup Winners Cup Final but lost to which team?

a) Monaco   b) Juventus   c) Valencia

9. How did they lose the final?

a) A toss up   b) After extra time   c) Penalties

10. Who did Terry sign in 1983 for £800,000?

a)   Charlie Nicholas b) Pat Jennings   c) Lee Chapman

QUIZ 5: BERTIE MEE

1.   What honour from the Queen was Mee awarded?

a)   OBE   b) MBE   c) CBE

2.   What position did Mee hold at the club before becoming manager?

a)   Director   b) Scout   c) Physio

3.   In 1970 Mee led Arsenal to their first European success winning the Inter Cities Fairs Cup but how did teams initially qualify for it?

a)   Capital city team   b) Holding a trade fair   c) Winning cup competition

4.   When the Inter Cities Fairs Cup was rebranded what was it called?

a)   Champions League   b) Cup Winners Cup   c) UEFA Cup

5.   They beat Anderlecht over two legs in the final, what was the aggregate score?

a)   4-3   b) 3-2   c) 4-0

6.   In 1971 Mee won the League and Cup double. Who did they beat in the final of the FA Cup?

a)   Swindon Town b) Liverpool   c) Manchester United

7.   At the time it was only the second time the League and Cup double had been achieved. Who was the first?

a)   Liverpool   b) Manchester United   c) Tottenham Hotspur

8. **How many years was Mee manager of Arsenal?**
a) 9   b) 11   c) 13

9. **After resigning from Arsenal which club Bertie join as assistant manager?**
a) Watford   b) Crystal Palace   c) Everton

10. **When Mee resigned from Arsenal, he held the record for the most number of wins. Who broke this record?**
a) Arsene Wenger   b) George Graham   c) Terry Neill

QUIZ 6: UNAI EMERY

1. **What club was Emery manager of prior to Arsenal?**
a) Sevilla   b) PSG   c) AC Milan

2. **What nationality is Emery?**
a) Spanish   b) Portuguese   c) Argentinian

3. **What was the score in his first Premier League match against Manchester City?**
a) 0-0   b) 1-1   c) 0-2

4. **Which team did Emery's first win come against?**
a) Newcastle United   b) West Ham United   c) Burnley

5. **What was Emery's win percentage while at Arsenal?**
a) 35%   b) 45%   c) 55%

6. **At which club did Emery win the Europa League 3 times?**
a) Sevilla   b) Valencia   c) PSG

7. In the 2018/19 season Emery lead Arsenal to the Europa League final but which team did they lose to?

a) Chelsea   b) Lyon   c) Atletico Madrid

8. Who was Emery's most expensive signing?

a) David Luiz   b) Nicolas Pepe   c) Kieran Tierney

9. What is Emery's longest stay at a club as a manger?

a) 3 years   b) 4 years   c) 5 years

10. Emery was fired after his team lost at home in the Europa League, but who were the opponents?

a) Standard Liege   b) Vitoria SC   c) Eintracht Frankfurt

QUIZ 7: MIKEL ARTETA

1. What year was Arteta born?

a) 1976   b) 1979   c) 1982

2. Which Scottish team did he join as a player?

a) Celtic   b) Rangers   c) Hearts

3. What nationality is Arteta?

a) Spanish   b) French   c) Italian

4. In what year did Arteta sign for Arsenal?

a) 2010   b) 2011   c) 2012

5. From which Premier League club did Arsenal sign Arteta as a player?

a) Manchester City   b) Liverpool   c) Everton

6. How much did he cost?

a) £5 million   b) £10 million   c) £15 million

7. How many goals did Arteta score for Arsenal?

a) 14   b) 24   c) 34

8. How many appearances did he make in his 5 years at the club?
    a) 110   b) 125   c) 140

9. What club did they sign Mikel from as a manager?
    a) Manchester City   b) Liverpool   c) Everton

10. Who were his first opponents as a manger?
    a) Norwich City   b) Chelsea   c) Bournemouth

QUIZ 8: CHARLIE NICHOLAS

1. What position did Nicholas play?
a)   Defender   b) Midfield   c) Striker

2. What club did Nicholas start his professional career at?
a)   Rangers   b) Celtic   c) Clyde

3. In what year did he make his international debut for Scotland?
a)   1981   b) 1983   c) 1985

4. Nicholas scored on his international debut in a 2-2 draw but who were the opposition?
a)   Switzerland   b) England   c) Portugal

5. Which manager signed Nicholas for Arsenal?
a)   Terry Neill   b) George Graham   c) Bertie Mee

6. In what year did he sign for Arsenal?
a)   1982   b) 1983   c) 1984

7. What was the transfer fee paid by Arsenal?
a)   £50,000   b) £250,000   c) £750,000

8. Nicholas scored on his debut in his second game for the club in August. When did he score his second goal for Arsenal?
a)   October   b) November   c) December

9. **How did he score his first goal at Highbury?**
a) *Penalty* b) *Free Kick* c) *Header*

10. **What nickname was given to Charlie while at Arsenal?**
    a) *Champion* b) *Champagne* c) *Cockney*

QUIZ 9: PAT JENNINGS

1. **Which award was Jennings given by the Queen?**
a) *MBE*   b) *CBE*   c) *OBE*

2. **He played for Shamrock under 18s as an 11-year-old, but then decided to concentrate on what other sport?**
a) *Gaelic Football*   b) *Cricket*   c) *Hurling*

3. **What English league team was his first senior club?**
a) *Crystal Palace*   b) *Tottenham Hotspur* c) *Watford*

4. **Jennings made his international debut for Northern Ireland at the age of 18 in the British Home Championship against which team?**
a) *England*   b) *Wales*   c) *Scotland*

5. **Which club did Arsenal sign Jennings from?**
a) *Watford*   b) *Chelsea*   c) *Tottenham Hotspur*

6. **In 1976 Jennings was the first ever goalkeeper to claim which award?**
a) *Football Writers Player of the Year*   b) *PFA player of the Year*
    c) *Ballon Dor*

7. **How many years did Jennings play for Arsenal?**
a) *4*   b) *6*   c) *8*

8. **How many trophies did he win with Arsenal?**
a) *1*   b) *2*   c) *3*

9. Who were the opponents in Pat's last professional game?

a) Brazil   b) Colombia   c) Mexico

10. In which year was Jennings inducted into the English Football Hall of Fame?

a) 2003   b) 2005   c) 2007

QUIZ 10: THIERRY HENRY

1. What is Thierry's middle name?

a) Jacques   b) Paul   c) Daniel

2. At which team did Henry makes his professional debut?

a) Monaco   b) PSG   c) Lyon

3. From which club did Arsenal sign Henry?

a) Monaco   b) Barcelona   c) Juventus

4. What was the fee paid by Arsenal to sign Henry?

a) £9 million   b) £11 million   c) £13 million

5. Henry made 377 appearances for Arsenal but how many goals did he score?

a) 204   b) 216   c) 228

6. In which of Henry's seasons with Arsenal did he win his first silverware?

a) First Season   b) Second Season   c) Third Season

7. Henry became Arsenals top goal scorer of all time during the 05-06 season, but whose record did he beat?

a) Ian Wright   b) Cliff Bastin   c) John Radford

8. Between 2003 and 2004 Arsenal went 49 league games without being beaten. Thierry played in 48 of these games, but how many goals did he score in those games?

a) 29   b) 34   c) 39

9. At which American team did Henry finish his career?

a) Seattle Sounders   b) New York Red Bulls   c) LA Galaxy

10. In 2018 he took his first head managerial role at which club?

a) Montreal Impact   b) Monaco   c) Mainz

QUIZ 11: DENNIS BERGKAMP

1. What nationality is Bergkamp?

a) Danish   b) Dutch   c) Swedish

2. What did Dennis have a fear of?

a) Heights   b) Enclosed Spaces   c) Flying

3. What year did Bergkamp join Arsenal?

a) 1991   b) 1993   c) 1995

4. His father named him Dennis after which former footballer?

a) Denis Law   b) Dennis Allen   c) Dennis Taylor

5. In what year did he make his professional debut for Ajax?

a) 1984   b) 1986   c) 1988

6. From which club did Arsenal sign Bergkamp?

a) Ajax   b) AC Milan   c) Inter Milan

7. Who was the manager when Bergkamp signed for Arsenal?

a) Arsene Wenger   b) Bruce Rioch   c) George Graham

8. Bergkamp scored his 100th goal for Arsenal in the FA Cup in the 2002-03 season. Who were the opponents?

a) Oxford United   b) Crewe Alexandra   c) Leyton Orient

9. Bergkamp's testimonial was the first game held at the Emirates Stadium but who were the opponents?

a) Inter Milan   b) Tottenham Hotspurs   c) Ajax

10. In what year did Bergkamp come first, second and third in the goal of the month competition?

a) 1997   b) 1998   c) 1999

QUIZ 12: TONY ADAMS

1. Where was Adams born?

a) Guildford   b) Romford   c) Dagenham

2. How many clubs did Adams play for?

a) 1   b) 2   c) 3

3. How old was Adams when he made his first team debut for Arsenal?

a) 16   b) 17   c) 18

4. Which manager gave Adams his debut?

a) George Graham   b) Don Howe   c) Terry Neill

5. How many appearances did he make for Arsenal?

a) 572   b) 622   c) 672

6. How many Premier League and First Division titles did he win at Arsenal?

a) 3   b) 4   c) 5

7. **After retiring he went into coaching and managing, but which club was his first managerial position?**

a) *Granada* b) *Portsmouth* c) *Wycombe Wanderers*

8. **He has been manager of clubs for a total of 82 games, how many of those games has he won?**

a) *16* b) *26* c) *36*

9. **In May 1998 he brought out his critically acclaimed autobiography, what was the title?**

a) *Offside Trap* b) *Addicted* c) *Stopper*

10. **In 2019 he became president of which sporting body?**

a) *England Cricket Board* b) *Football Association* c) *Rugby Football League*

QUIZ 13: IAN WRIGHT

1. **Where did Wright start his professional career?**

a) *QPR* b) *Watford* c) *Crystal Palace*

2. **How much did Arsenal pay to sign Wright in 1991?**

a) *£2 million* b) *£2.5 million* c) *£3 million*

3. **How many goals did he score on his league debut against Southampton?**

a) *1* b) *2* c) *3*

4. **In his first season with Arsenal he was the league's top scorer with how many goals?**

a) *29* b) *32* c) *35*

5. **Who was manager when Wright handed in a transfer request?**

a) *George Graham* b) *Bruce Rioch* c) *Arsene Wenger*

6. **For which non-English club did he make 8 appearances?**

a) *Celtic* b) *Rangers* c) *Cardiff*

7. **In 2000 which order of chivalry did he receive from the Queen?**

a) *CBE*   b) *OBE*   c) *MBE*

8. **Wright played 288 times for Arsenal, how many goals did he score?**

a) *159*   b) *172*   c) *185*

9. **His sons Bradley and Shaun both played for the same club at different times, but what club?**

a) *QPR*   b) *Manchester City*   c) *New York Red Bulls*

10. **Which sports brand used the slogan 'Behind every goalkeeper there's a ball from Ian Wright'?**

a) *Nike*   b) *Adidas*   c) *Umbro*

QUIZ 14: EMIRATES STADIUM

1. **How far is the Emirates stadium from Highbury?**

a) *150m*   b) *450m*   c) *750m*

2. **How much did the government give towards the building of the stadium?**

a) *£0*   b) *£50 million*   c) *£100 million*

3. **What is the record attendance at The Emirates?**

a) *57,992*   b) *60,161*   c) *62,897*

4. **Who were Arsenals opponents in their first competitive game at the Emirates?**

a) *Newcastle United*   b) *Blackburn Rovers*   c) *Aston Villa*

5. **Who scored the first competitive goal in this game?**

a) *Olof Mellberg*   b) *Gilberto Silva*   c) *Lee Hendrie*

6. **Which international football team has used the stadium to host international friendlies?**
a) *France* *b) USA* *c) Brazil*

7. **How big is the field size at the Emirates?**
a) *102m x 59m* *b) 103m x 61m* *c) 105m x 68m*

8. **In 2008 the Emirates held a summit between Gordon Brown and which other world leader?**
a) *Nicolas Sarkozy* *b) Angela Merkel* *c) Silvio Berlusconi*

9. **What is Arsenal's largest margin of victory at the Emirates?**
a) *8-1* *b) 9-0* *c) 7-0*

10. **How much did the Emirates cost to build?**
a) *£350 million* *b) £390 million* *c) £430 million*

QUIZ 15: HIGHBURY

1. **When did Arsenal first use Highbury?**
a) *1900* *b) 1907* *c) 1913*

2. **In the first year at Highbury what were Arsenal not allowed to do?**
a) *Play in red shirts* *b) Serve alcohol* *c) Have corner flags*

3. **How much did Highbury cost to build?**
a) *£30,000* *b) £70,000* *c) £125,000*

4. **What was the record attendance at Highbury?**
a) *71,295* *b) 73,295* *c) 75,295*

5. **England used Highbury as the location to hold its first match against non-British and Irish opposition but who was it?**
a) *Belgium* *b) France* *c) Germany*

6. During the second world war Highbury was used as an air raid protection station and was subsequently bombed, so Arsenal could not use it to stage their matches. Where did they play instead?

a) Selhurst Park   b) White Hart Lane   c) Stamford Bridge

7. In 1966 Highbury hosted the world heavyweight boxing title bout between Muhammad Ali and Henry Cooper, but who won the fight?

a) Ali   b) Cooper   c) Draw

8. Which stand is a grade 2 listed building?

a) Clock End   b) East Stand   c) North Bank Stand

9. What was the name of the project that saw Highbury get redeveloped and converted into flats?

a) Highbury Square   b) The New Highbury   c) Highbury Heights

10. How many games did Arsenal play at Highbury?

a) 2010   b) 2110   c) 2210

QUIZ 16: 1960's TRANSFERS

1. In 1960 Arsenal purchased George Eastham after the player had taken his previous club to court after they denied his transfer request, what was the previous club?

a) Sunderland   b) Newcastle United   c) Middlesbrough

2. In 1961 which Scottish right half did Arsenal sell to Chelsea?

a) Tommy Docherty   b) Frank O'Neill   c) Fred Clarke

3. In July 1962 Billy Wright paid a club record fee of £70,000 for Joe Baker. From which Italian club was he signed?

a) Napoli   b) Parma   c) Torino

4. Arsenal signed Scottish international Bob Wilson, an amateur from Wolves in July 1963. What position did he play?

a) Goalkeeper   b) Midfield   c) Striker

5. Which player, signed for a club record in October 1964, went on to hand in a transfer request 2 years later, which was denied. He helped secure the clubs first major trophy in 17 years winning the Inter Cities Fairs Cup in 1970?

a) Peter Simpson   b) Frank McLintock   c) Charlie George

6. In 1966 Bertie Mee signed Colin Addison from Nottingham Forest for £45,000, how many seasons did he stay at Arsenal?

a) 1   b) 2   c) 3

7. Which future manager did Arsenal sign from Chelsea in 1966?

a) Bruce Rioch   b) Stuart Houston   c) George Graham

8. Which did club Arsenal buy Bobby Gould from in 1968 for £90,000?

a) Birmingham City   b) Coventry City   c) Leeds United

9. In 1969 Arsenal sold Ian Ure to Manchester United for what fee?

a) £60,000   b) £80,000   c) £100,000

10. Geoff Barnett was signed in October 1969 after an injury to which key player?

a) Bob Wilson   b) Pat Rice   c) Frank McLintock

Quiz 17: 1970's Transfers

1. In January 1970 Arsenal paid a six figure sum for the first time to buy Peter Marinello from which Scottish club?

a) Aberdeen   b) Hearts   c) Hibernian

2. **Which 1966 world cup winner did Arsenal sign on 22ⁿᵈ December 1971 for club record £220,000?**

a) Alan Ball   b) Geoff Hurst   c) Martin Peters

3. **In 1972 George Graham was sold for £120,000 to which club?**

a) Tottenham Hotspur   b) Leeds United   c) Manchester United

4. **Jimmy Rimmer signed for Arsenal in 1974 as a long term replacement for Bob Wilson, but only played once in that season. How many goals did he concede in that game?**

a) 0   b) 2   c) 4

5. **From which relegated club did Brian Kidd join Arsenal?**

a) Manchester United   b) Everton   c) Manchester City

6. **Youth team graduate Ray Kennedy, who played 213 times scoring 71 goals for Arsenal, was sold to Liverpool in July 1974 for what price?**

a) £150,000   b) £200,000   c) £250,000

7. **In August 1977 Pat Jennings signed for Arsenal from Tottenham and played for 8 years. What country in the UK was he born?**

a) Northern Ireland   b) Wales   c) Scotland

8. **Alan Sunderland joined Arsenal for £220,000 in November 1977 from which club?**

a) Leeds United   b) Ipswich Town   c) Wolverhampton Wanderers

9. **Which player joined Arsenal in January 1979 for a fee of £450,000 and played 327 times scoring 49 goals from midfield?**

a) Mark Heeley   b) Brian Talbot   c) Liam Brady

10. **In 1979 Alan Hudson joined which American team for £100,000 after having differences with manager Terry Neill?**

a) LA Galaxy   b) Seattle Sounders   c) Los Angeles Aztecs

QUIZ 18: 1980's TRANSFER

1. **Who did Arsenal sign in 1980 for £1.25 million and played 3 friendlies and 0 competitive games and was sold to Crystal Palace the same year?**
    a) *Clive Allen*   b) *George Wood*   c) *Chris Whyte*

2. **Kenny Samson joined in the summer of 1980 from which club?**
    a) *QPR*   b) *Newcastle United*   c) *Crystal Palace*

3. **Frank Stapleton was sold in 1981 to Manchester United for what fee?**
    a) *£500,000*   b) *£700,000*   c) *£900,000*

4. **Who joined Arsenal from Celtic for £750,000 on 22ⁿᵈ June 1983 reportedly becoming the highest paid footballer?**
    a) *Paul Merson*   b) *Charlie Nicholas*   c) *Lee Chapman*

5. **Tommy Caton was signed from which club in 1983?**
    a) *Manchester City*   b) *Manchester United*   c) *Liverpool*

6. **Martin Keown was sent out on loan in 1985 to which club?**
    a) *Brighton & Hove Albion*   b) *Southampton*   c) *Portsmouth*

7. **Which England international did Arsenal sign from Nottingham Forest in 1984? He went on to play for Manchester United, Sheffield Wednesday, Barnsley and Middlesbrough.**
    a) *Steve Williams*   b) *Nigel Winterburn*   c) *Viv Anderson*

8. **In what year did Lee Dixon join the club from Stoke City?**
    a) *1988*   b) *1989*   c) *1990*

9. **Which winger joined Arsenal from Sheffield Wednesday in March 1988, won the First Division title in his first year, and was described by Alan Smith as the most prolific supplier of assists while he was at Arsenal?**
    a) *Martin Hayes*   b) *Brian Marwood*   c) *Perry Groves*

10. Arsenal signed Steve Bould in 1988 for £390,000 from which club?

a) *Stoke City*   b) *Sunderland*   c) *West Ham United*

QUIZ 19: 1990'S TRANSFERS

1. In March 1990 Arsenal sold Niall Quinn for £800,000 to which club?

a) *Sunderland*   b) *Liverpool*   c) *Manchester City*

2. Who did George Graham sign in 1990 from Queens Park Rangers?

a) *Ray Parlour*   b) *David Seaman*   c) *Paul Dickov*

3. Which former Arsenal academy player and future England international was sold to Bristol City in 1992?

a) *Andy Cole*   b) *Michael Thomas*   c) *Kevin Campbell*

4. 1995 saw the arrival of Dennis Bergkamp from which Italian club?

a) *AC Milan*   b) *Juventus*   c) *Inter Milan*

5. What was Bergkamp's transfer fee?

a) *£3.5 million*   b) *£5 million*   c) *£7.5 million*

6. David Platt also joined in 1995 for £4.75 million from which Italian club?

a) *Sampdoria*   b) *Bari*   c) *Juventus*

7. In what year did Patrick Vieira join Arsenal?

a) *1996*   b) *1997*   c) *1998*

8. Arsenal signed Petit, Overmars, Upson, Anelka, Boa Morte and Grimandi all in what year?

a) *1996*   b) *1997*   c) *1998*

9. **Legend Ian Wright left in 1998 to join which club?**

a) *West Ham United*   b) *Crystal Palace*   c) *Celtic*

10. **In August 1999 Thierry Henry joined Arsenal from which club?**

a) *PSG*   b) *Monaco*   c) *Juventus*

QUIZ 20: 2000'S TRANSFERS

1. **Lauren was the first signing for the club in 2000, but what club did he join from?**

a) *Mallorca*   b) *Real Sociedad*   c) *Athletic Bilbao*

2. **On the 3rd July 2000 Arsenal signed Robert Pires from Marseille. How many Arsenal appearances did he make?**

a) *274*   b) *287*   c) *300*

3. **In 2001 Sol Campbell joined from Tottenham, how much did he cost?**

a) *Free*   b) *£5 million*   c) *£10 million*

4. **On the 1st July 2003 Arsenal brought in Cesc Fabregas from which Spanish club?**

a) *Real Madrid*   b) *Barcelona*   c) *Sevilla*

5. **Nwankwo Kanu was sold to which club in 2004?**

a) *Everton*   b) *Portsmouth*   c) *West Bromwich Albion*

6. **On 20th January 2006 Arsenal signed Theo Walcott from Southampton for £5 million rising to £12 millon depending on appearances. How old was he when he signed for Arsenal?**

a) *15*   b) *16*   c) *17*

7. **Which club signed Patrick Vieira from Arsenal in the summer of 2005?**

a) *Juventus*   b) *Inter Milan*   c) *AC Milan*

8. Ashley Cole signed for Chelsea in August 2006 after a long and bitter saga with Arsenal. He earned the nickname 'Cashley' from the Arsenal fans. He was sold for £5 million plus which player from Chelsea?

a) *Samir Nasri*   b) *Lassana Diarra*   c) *William Gallas*

9. On the 13th June 2008 Arsenal signed Aaron Ramsey from which club?

a) *Cardiff*   b) *Wrexham*   c) *Swansea*

10. In the summer of 2009 Arsenal sold Emmanuel Adebayor to Manchester City for what fee?

a) *£25 million*   b) *£30 million*   c) *£35 million*

QUIZ 21: 2010'S TRANSFERS

1. Sol Campbell joined Arsenal for the second time in January 2010, which club did he join from?

a) *Portsmouth*   b) *Notts County*   c) *Newcastle*

2. On the 31st August 2011 Arsenal signed German defender Per Mertesacker from which club?

a) *Werder Bremen*   b) *Schalke*   c) *Bayer Leverkusen*

3. Arsenal signed Hector Bellerin in 2012 from which league club?

a) *Leeds United*   b) *Sheffield Wednesday*   c) *Barnsley*

4. On 2nd September 2013 Arsenal purchased Mesut Ozil from Real Madrid for what fee?

a) *£27.5 million*   b) *£35 million*   c) *£42.5 million*

5. Thomas Vermaelen left in 2014 to join which Spanish team? He made 53 appearances for them, 34 in the league, between 2014 and 2019.

a) *Barcelona*   b) *Real Madrid*   c) *Valencia*

6. **In 2016 Arsenal purchased Granit Xhaka from Borrusia Monchengladbach, which national team does he play for?**

a) Poland   b) Switzerland   c) Croatia

7. **Lukas Podolski left in 2015 to join which Turkish club?**

a) Besiktas   b) Galatasaray   c) Fenerbache

8. **Pierre-Emerick Aubameyang was bought in 2018 for £56 million, a club record at the time, from which German club?**

a) Borussia Dortmund   b) Bayern Munich   c) Wolfsburg

9. **On the 5th July 2017 Arsenal signed Alexandre Lacazette from Lyon, but prior to this Lyon had verbally agreed to sell him to a Spanish club which fell through after this club had a transfer ban upheld. Which club was it?**

a) Athletico Madrid   b) Barcelona   c) Real Madrid

10. **In 2019 Nicolas Pepe was purchased from Lille for a club record fee. What was the fee?**

a) £70 million   b) £72 million   c) £74 million

QUIZ 22: FIRST DIVISION WINNERS 1952 – 53

1. **How many games did Arsenal lose in the 42 game winning 1952 – 53 season?**

a) 3   b) 6   c) 9

2. **First and second place were equal on points. How was the title was decided?**

a) Goal difference   b) Goal Per Game Average   c) Goal ratio

3. **Who scored the most league goals for Arsenal during the season?**

a) Doug Lishman   b) Cliff Holton   c) Don Roper

4. **Arsenal's biggest away victory was 5-1 over which unfortunate victims?**

a) *Chelsea*   b) *Liverpool*   c) *Tottenham Hotspurs*

5. **Which team finished second in the league that season level on points with Arsenal?**

a) *Preston North End*   b) *Chelsea*   c) *Wolverhampton Wanderers*

6. **This League title was a record for the most First Division Championships. How many had they won at this point?**

a) *5*   b) *7*   c) *9*

7. **They won the Community Shield in 1953 playing the winners of the FA Cup, but who were their opponents?**

a) *Preston North End*   b) *Sheffield Wednesday*   c) *Blackpool*

8. **Which Welsh international played 41 of the 42 league games at centre half this season?**

a) *Ray Daniel*   b) *Alex Forbes*   c) *Jack Kelsey*

9. **Who was the Arsenal manager this season?**

a) *George Allison*   b) *Tom Whittaker*   c) *Jack Crayston*

10. **After reaching the FA Cup final in two of the previous three seasons they were knocked out by the eventual winners in the quarter finals. Which team knocked them out?**

a) *Blackpool*   b) *Preston*   c) *Aston Villa*

QUIZ 23: INTER CITIES FAIRS CUP WINNERS 1969-70

1. **Who were the defending champions in the Inter Cities Fairs Cup competition of 1969-70?**

a) *Rangers*   b) *Newcastle United*   c) *Leeds United*

2. **Who was the leading goal scorer for Arsenal in the competition?**

a) *George Graham*   b) *John Radford*   c) *Jon Sammels*

3. **Who were Arsenal's opponents in the final?**
a) Anderlecht   b) Inter Milan   c) Ajax

4. **The final was played over two legs, one home and one away. What was the aggregate score after both legs?**
a) 5-0   b) 4-3   c) 2-1

5. **Who was the captain of Arsenal?**
a) Bob Wilson   b) Frank McLintock   c) George Graham

6. **Who scored Arsenal's goal in the first leg of the final?**
a) John Radford   b) Charlie George   c) Ray Kennedy

7. **Who was Arsenal's manager this season?**
a) Bertie Mee   b) Terry Neill   c) Billy Wright

8. **Who did Arsenal play in the semi final, losing 1-0 away and winning 3-0 at home?**
a) Ajax   b) Sporting CP   c) Napoli

9. **In defending their cup in the 1970 – 71 competition they were beaten by whom?**
a) Bayern Munich   b) Hamburger FC   c) FC Koln

10. **Their largest win came in the quarter finals with a 9-1 aggregate win over Dinamo Bacau. They won 2-0 away and 7-1 at home, but what country are Dinamo Bacau from?**
a) Hungary   b) Romania   c) Bulgaria

QUIZ 24: FA CUP WINNERS 1970-71

1. **Who did Arsenal beat 2-1 in the final?**
a) Manchester United   b) Newcastle United   c) Liverpool

2. **What was the Arsenal manager in the final?**
a) Bertie Mee   b) Terry Neill   c) Don Howe

3. **Who were the FA Cup defending champions this year?**
a) *Leeds United* b) *Manchester City* c) *Chelsea*

4. **The first goal in the final was scored by a substitute for the first time. Who netted for the Gunners?**
a) *Bob McNab*   b) *Eddie Kelly*   c) *Peter Marinello*

5. **Which Arsenal player scored the winner in extra time?**
a) *Charlie George*   b) *George Graham*   c) *Ray Kennedy*

6. **Arsenal achieved the League and Cup double this year. Which team did the feat ten years prior to Arsenal?**
a) *Manchester United* b) *Preston North End* c) *Tottenham Hotspur*

7. **Who was the Arsenal goalkeeper in the final?**
a) *Bob Wilson* b) *Jimmy Rimmer* c) *Geoff Barnett*

8. **Arsenal needed a replay in the semi final to beat which team?**
a) *Everton*   b) *Stoke City*   c) *Leicester City*

9. **Which player who played in the final was sold to their opponents in July 1974 for £20,000?**
a) *John Radford*   b) *Ray Kennedy*   c) *George Armstrong*

10. **How many Scotsmen were in the final starting XI for Arsenal?**
a) *1*   b) *2*   c) *3*

QUIZ 25: FIRST DIVISION WINNERS 1970-71

1. **Who finished runners up to Arsenal?**
a) *Tottenham Hotspurs* b) *Wolverhampton Wanderers* c) *Leeds United*

2. **On 26th September 1970 Arsenal suffered their largest away defeat of the season, who were they opponents?**
a) *Stoke City* b) *Crystal Palace* c) *Ipswich Town*

3. Arsenal conceded just 29 goals in 42 games and had the season's second best defensive record. Who had the best record?

a) Liverpool b) Southampton c) Chelsea

4. How many clean sheets did the Gunners keep in the league season?

a) 20 b) 22 c) 25

5. Between 23rd February 1971 and 22nd April 1971 Arsenal played nine games conceding only one goal in that time. They conceded the goal against Southampton but who was the scorer?

a) Mick Channon b) Ron Davies c) Terry Paine

6. Arsenal sealed the league title on the last day of the season with a win against Tottenham at White Hart Lane. Who scored the winning goal?

a) Charlie George b) George Armstrong c) Ray Kennedy

7. On 19th September 1970 Arsenal had their highest scoring game of the season beating which team 6-2?

a) Burnley b) West Bromwich Albion c) Nottingham Forest

8. Which team was the only team the Gunners failed to secure a victory over in the league this season?

a) Leeds United b) Liverpool c) Wolverhampton Wanderers

9. By winning the league Arsenal qualified for the European Cup. What round were they knocked out?

a) Second Round b) Quarter Finals c) Semi Finals

10. They were knocked out after losing 2-1 away and 1-0 at home to which team?

a) Ajax b) Celtic c) Benfica

QUIZ 26: FA CUP WINNERS 1978-79

1. **How many games did Arsenal play in the third round?**
   a) 2   b) 3   c) 5

2. **Who were there opponents in the third round?**
   a) Aston Villa   b) Liverpool   c) Sheffield Wednesday

3. **The Gunners were entered into the third round of the FA Cup as is standard for top division teams. How many games did they play total to win the FA Cup this season?**
   a) 9   b) 10   c) 11

4. **Who were joint top scorers in the cup that year for Arsenal?**
   a) Frank Stapleton & Alan Sunderland   b) Alan Sunderland & Liam Brady   c) Liam Brady & Frank Stapleton

5. **Who did Arsenal beat 2-0 in the semi final?**
   a) Liverpool   b) Wolverhampton Wanderers   c) Southampton

6. **Which ground hosted the semi final?**
   a) Maine Road   b) Goodison Park   c) Villa Park

7. **Who was the manager of Arsenal in the final?**
   a) Terry Neill   b) Don Howe   c) George Graham

8. **Who were their opponents in the final?**
   a) Manchester United   b) Chelsea   c) Tottenham Hotspurs

9. **Who scored a last minute winner to stop the match going into extra time?**
   a) Alan Sunderland   b) Frank Stapleton   c) Liam Brady

10. **What was the nickname given to the final?**
    a) The Grand Finale   b) The Dirty Final   c) The 5 minute final

QUIZ 27: FIRST DIVISION WINNERS 1988-89

1. Before the season began the FA made a big change to English football by selling the rights to league games to which television organisation?

    a) BBC   b) ITV   c) Sky

2. What was the result in the first North London derby to be held at Wembley in the Wembley International Tournament?

    a) Arsenal Win   b) Draw   c) Tottenham Win

3. Who did Arsenal beat 3-0 to win the tournament?

    a) Sampdoria   b) AC Milan   c) Bayern Munich

4. Who finished second in the league, behind Arsenal, this season?

    a) Nottingham Forest   b) Liverpool   c) Norwich City

5. The first fixture was away at Plough Lane resulting in 5-1 win but who were the opponents?

    a) Derby County   b) Charlton Athletic   c) Wimbledon

6. Who was the top scorer in the league for Arsenal?

    a) Alan Smith   b) Brian Marwood   c) Paul Merson

7. Arsenal's biggest win of the season came on the 1st May 1989 against Norwich, what was the score?

    a) 5-0   b) 6-0   c) 7-1

8. Who was the club captain for the 1988/89 season?

    a) Paul Merson   b) Tony Adams   c) Steve Bould

9. Arsenal were in second place going into the last game against Liverpool, who were top. Arsenal won the game 2-0 with a last minute goal from Michael Thomas. Why was the last minute goal so important?

a) *Arsenal won the league on goal difference*   b) *Arsenal won the league on combined score against Liverpool*   c) *Arsenal won the league on goals scored*

10. **However, the 1988/89 season will be forever remembered for what?**
a) *Hillsborough Disaster*   b) *Bradford City Fire*   c) *Heysel Stadium Disaster*

QUIZ 28: FA CUP WINNERS 1992-93

1. **Arsenal won the 1993 FA Cup final after a replay and extra time. Who did they beat?**
a) *Aston Villa*   b) *Birmingham*   c) *Sheffield Wednesday*

2. **These two teams met in another competition this season. Which competition?**
a) *League Cup*   b) *Inter Cities Fairs Cup*   c) *Charity Shield*

3. **The 1993 cup final replay saw the last game for Arsenal for which stalwart who had been at club for 18 years?**
a) *David O'Leary*   b) *George Armstrong*   c) *Pat Rice*

4. **What was unique about the 1993 final?**
a) *First to use yellow and red cards*   b) *Last final decided by a replay*   c) *Last to have just one substitute*

5. **Who scored Arsenal's winning goal in the replay?**
a) *Tony Adams*   b) *Paul Merson*   c) *Andy Linighan*

6. **Why was the replay memorable for Alan Smith?**
a) *He missed the first ever FA Cup final penalty*   b) *He received his one and only yellow card*   c) *He broke his nose*

7. **John Jensen played for Arsenal in the final. What nationality is he?**
a) *Danish*   b) *Swedish*   c) *Norweigan*

8. **Who did Arsenal defeat 1-0 in the semi final?**

a) *Chelsea*   b) *Crystal Palace*   c) *Tottenham Hotspur*

9. **Who was Arsenal's leading scorer in their 1992-93 FA Cup campaign?**

a) *Kevin Campbell*   b) *Ian Wright*   c) *Alan Smith*

10. **Who was Arsenal's manager for the final?**

a) *Don Howe*   b) *George Graham*   c) *Bruce Rioch*

QUIZ 29: PREMIER LEAGUE WINNERS 2001-02

1. **Who were Arsenal's shirt sponsor this year?**

a) *JVC*   b) *Dreamcast*   c) *O2*

2. **Arsenal lost three home games in the league this season. How many away games did they lose?**

a) *0*   b) *1*   c) *2*

3. **Which Arsenal player was named player of the season?**

a) *Thierry Henry*   b) *Freddie Ljungberg*   c) *Sol Campbell*

4. **Which team finished second in the league?**

a) *Liverpool*   b) *Manchester United*   c) *Newcastle United*

5. **How many French players were in the squad and played at least one game as a substitute or a starter?**

a) *4*   b) *5*   c) *6*

6. **Can you name all the French players?**

7. **In all competitions this season which player was sent off three times?**

a) *Patrick Vieria*   b) *Martin Keown*   c) *Ray Parlour*

8. **Which two players announced their retirement from playing at the end of the season with a combined 1288 appearances for the club?**

a) *Martin Keown and Tony Adams*   b) *Tony Adams and Lee Dixon*
c) *Martin Keown and Lee Dixon*

9. **Arsenal won a double this year but what was the other trophy they won?**

a) *Champions League*   b) *League Cup*   c) *FA Cup*

10. **Who did Arsenal beat to clinch the title with a game to go?**

a) *Bolton Wanderers*   b) *Everton*   c) *Manchester United*

QUIZ 30: FA CUP WINNERS 2002-03

1. **Arsenal beat Southampton in the final 1-0 but who scored the winning goal?**

b) *Thierry Henry*   b) *Dennis Bergkamp*   c) *Robert Pires*

2. **Who were the defending champions from the 2001-02 season?**

b) *Chelsea*   b) *Manchester United*   c) *Arsenal*

3. **Who was Southampton's manager in the final?**

b) *Gordon Strachan*   b) *Glenn Hoddle*   c) *Harry Redknapp*

4. **Where was the final played?**

b) *Wembley*   b) *Principality Stadium*   c) *Millennium Stadium*

5. **Who was the only Cameroonian in the Arsenal squad for the final?**

b) *Nwankwo Kanu*   b) *Lauren*   c) *Kolo Toure*

6. **Who was the captain of the Gunners in the final?**

a) *Patrick Vieira*   b) *Sol Campbell*   c) *David Seaman*

7. **Which Arsenal stalwart played their last game for the club in the final after making 564 appearances for the club?**

 a) Martin Keown   b) David Seaman   c) Ray Parlour

8. **Who was man of the match in the final?**

 a) Thierry Henry   b) Dennis Bergkamp   c) Freddie Ljungberg

9. **David Seaman said the disappointment of losing out in the league, they finished second, had spurred them on to win the final. Who won the league this season?**

 a) Chelsea   b) Blackburn Rovers   c) Manchester United

10. **How many times did Arsene Wenger win the FA Cup with Arsenal?**

 a) 5   b) 6   c) 7

QUIZ 31: CLUB CAPTAINS

1. **Who was the Arsenal captain from 1967-73?**

 a) Frank McLintock   b) George Graham   c) John Radford

2. **Who was the Arsenal captain from1976 to 1980?**

 a) Malcolm McDonald   b) Jimmy Rimmer   c) Pat Rice

3. **Who was the Arsenal captain from 1983 to 1986?**

 a) Graham Rix   b) Viv Anderson   c) Kenny Sansom

4. **Who was Arsenal captain from 6th March 1988 to 2002?**

 a) Martin Keown   b) Tony Adams   c) Lee Dixon

5. **Who was Arsenal captain from 2002 to 2005?**

 a) Patrick Vieira   b) Thierry Henry   c) Dennis Bergkamp

6. **Who was Arsenal captain from 2008 to 2011?**

 a) Cesc Fabregas   b) William Gallas   c) Samir Nasri

7. **Who was Arsenal captain in the 2011-12 season?**

a) *Robin van Persie* b) *Wojciech Szczesny* c) *Aaron Ramsey*

8. **Who was Arsenal captain from 2014 to 2016?**

a) *Oliver Giroud* b) *Alexis Sanchez* c) *Mikel Arteta*

9. **Who was Arsenal captain from 2016 to 2018?**

a) *Petr Cech* b) *Per Mertesacker* c) *Mesut Ozil*

10. **Who was Arsenal captain from 2018-2019?**

a) *Laurent Koscielny* b) *Bernd Leno* c) *Granit Xhaka*

QUIZ 32: PLAYER OF THE YEAR WINNERS

1. **Who was player of the season in 2005 – 06?**

a) *Sol Campbell* b) *Gilberto Silva* c) *Thierry Henry*

2. **Who was player of the season in 2006 - 07, 2007 - 08 and 2009 - 10?**

a) *Cesc Fabregas* b) *Kolo Toure* c) *Mikel Arteta*

3. **Who was player of the season in 2008 - 09 and 2011 - 12?**

a) *Tomas Rosicky* b) *Robin van Persie* c) *Theo Walcott*

4. **Who was player of the season in 2010 – 11?**

a) *Andrei Arshavin* b) *Laurent Koscielny* c) *Jack Wilshere*

5. **Who was player of the season in 2012 – 13?**

a) *Santi Cazorla* b) *Per Mertesacker* c) *Lukas Podolski*

6. **Who was player of the season in 2013 – 14 and 2017 - 18?**

a) *Hector Bellerin* b) *Olivier Giroud* c) *Aaron Ramsey*

7. **Who was player of the season in 2014 – 15 and 2016 - 17?**

a) *Alexis Sanchez* b) *Mathieu Flamini* c) *Nacho Monreal*

8. **Who was player of the season in 2015 - 16?**

a) Mesut Ozil   b) Petr Cech   c) Alex Oxlade-Chamberlain

9. **Who was player of the season in 2018 – 19?**

a) Henrikh Mkhitaryan   b) Alex Iwobi   c) Alexandre Lacazette

10. **Who was player of the season in 2019 – 20?**

David Luiz   b) Pierre-Emerick Aubameyang   c) Bukayo Saka

QUIZ 33: PATRICK VIEIRA

1. **Where was Vieira born?**

a) Paris   b) Marseille   c) Senegal

2. **Which club did Vieira play for professionally first?**

a) Lyon   b) Cannes   c) Cognac

3. **Arsenal signed Vieira on the 14th August 1996 for £3.5m. Who did they sign him from?**

a) AC Milan   b) Juventus   c) Lazio

4. **Which manager signed him for Arsenal??**

a) Bruce Rioch   b) Arsene Wenger   c) Stewart Houston

5. **Vieira made a total of 406 appearances for Arsenal. How many goals did he score in those games?**

a) 33   b) 55   c) 77

6. **Vieira won the World Cup with France in 1998. Who did they beat in the final?**

a) Brazil   b) Italy   c) Spain

7. **How many games did he play for France?**

a) 86   b) 94   c) 107

8. On the 15th August 2005 Vieira was sold for over £13m to which club?

a) *Real Madrid*   b) *Juventus*   c) *Inter Milan*

9. On the 8th January 2010 Vieira signed for another Premier League team. Which one?

a) *Manchester City*   b) *Chelsea*   c) *Everton*

10. How many trophies did Vieira win at Arsenal?

a) *5*   b) *7*   c) *9*

QUIZ 34: DAVID SEAMAN

1. **Where was Seaman born?**
a) *Rotherham*   *b) Doncaster*   *c) Sheffield*

2. **What was his first professional club?**
a) *Sheffield Wednesday*   *b) Leeds United*   *c) Hull City*

3. **He was sold to Peterborough aged 19 for what transfer fee?**
a) *£4,000* *b) £40,000* *c) £400,000*

4. **Who was the Arsenal manager who bought Seaman in 1990?**
a) *Don Howe* *b) Bruce Rioch* *c) George Graham*

5. **His first season for Arsenal in 1990 – 91 saw them win the First Division title. How many goals did Seaman concede in the 38 game season?**
a) *18*   *b) 20*   *c) 22*

6. **How many times did Seaman play for the England first team?**
a) *65*   *b) 75*   *c) 85*

7. **In the summer of 2003 Seaman left Arsenal to join which club?**
a) *Everton* *b) Aston Villa*   *c) Manchester City*

8. **How many appearances did Seaman make for Arsenal?**
a) *469*   *b) 564*   *c) 621*

9. **Seaman produced his autobiography in 2000. What was it titled?**
a) *Invincible*   *b) Safe Hands*   *c) The Pony Tailed Gunner*

10. **Which popular game show has Seaman competed in?**
a) *Strictly Come Dancing*   *b) I'm A Celebrity*   *c) Dancing On Ice*

QUIZ 35: LIAM BRADY

1. **Where was Brady born?**
a) *Belfast*   b) *Cork*   c) *Dublin*

2. **Who was the Arsenal manager when he made his debut in 1973?**
a) *Bertie Mee*   b) *Terry Neill*   c) *George Graham*

3. **What year was he named PFA player of the year?**
a) *1976*   b) *1978*   c) *1979*

4. **How many games did he play for Arsenal?**
a) *307*   b) *356*   c) *402*

5. **How many goals did he score in those games?**
a) *46*   b) *59*   c) *67*

6. **How many trophies did Brady win with Arsenal?**
a) *0*   b) *1*   c) *2*

7. **In 1980 Brady left Arsenal and joined which club?**
a) *Roma*   b) *Napoli*   c) *Juventus*

8. **Which other English team did he play for?**
a) *Chelsea*   b) *West Ham United*   c) *Tottenham Hotspur*

9. **In 1990 he was appointed to his first managerial appointment with which team?**
a) *Celtic*   b) *Everton*   c) *Aston Villa*

10. **What was his nickname?**
a) *Larry*   b) *Chippy*   c) *Skippy*

QUIZ 36: ROBERT PIRES

1. **Which club did Pires make his senior debut with?**

   a) Nantes   b) Cannes   c) Metz

2. **In 2000 Arsenal purchased Pires for £6 million from which club?**

   a) Marseille   b) Monaco   c) PSG

3. **His first season for Arsenal was 2000 – 01. How many Frenchmen were in the Arsenal squad for that season?**

   a) 3   b) 4   c) 5

4. **In 2002 Pires missed the FA Cup Final and the World Cup Finals due to a serious cruciate ligament injury which he received while playing against which club?**

   a) Blackburn Rovers   b) Leeds United   c) Newcastle United

5. **Pires scored a hat trick in a 6 – 1 demolition of Southampton on the 7th May 2003. Which other Arsenal player got the other three goals?**

   a) Dennis Bergkamp   b) Jermaine Pennant   c) Sylvain Wiltord

6. **In the 2006 Champions League Final Pires was substituted in what minute of the game?**

   a) 18th   b) 64th   c) 106th

7. **Pires has a World Cup Winners medal from 1998 and a Euro 2000 Winners medal with France. Who did France beat in the final of the Euro 2000 competition?**

   a) Spain   b) Netherlands   c) Italy

8. **In May 2006 Pires left Arsenal to join which Spanish club?**

   a) Seville   b) Villareal   c) Barcelona

9. **How many games did Pires play for France?**

   a) 56   b) 64   c) 79

10. **Which club was the last professional club that Pires played for?**

a) *Aston Villa*   b) *Goa*   c) *Villareal*

QUIZ 37: CHARLIE GEORGE

1. **What is Charlie George's middle name?**

a) *Frederick*   b) *Walter*   c) *Alexander*

2. **How many games did he play for Arsenal?**

a) *179*   b) *246*   c) *302*

3. **In 1971 George scored the winning goal in the FA Cup Final to complete the double for Arsenal. Who did they beat in the final?**

a) *Liverpool*   b) *Everton*   c) *Derby County*

4. **In July 1975 George was sold to which club for £100,000?**

a) *Leicester City*   b) *Derby County*   c) *Sheffield Wednesday*

5. **He scored a hat trick in a UEFA Cup game for his new club against which team?**

a) *Barcelona*   b) *Bayern Munich*   c) *Real Madrid*

6. **In 1978 George went to play for an American team in the North American Soccer League. Which team??**

a) *Boston Minutemen*   b) *Minnesota Kicks*   c) *Philadelphia Atoms*

7. **How many times did George play for England?**

a) *1*   b) *10*   c) *20*

8. **In April 1980 George was involved in an accident. What did the accident involve?**

a) *A Horse*   b) *A Steam Engine*   c) *A Lawn Mower*

40

9. George played in the 1979 UEFA Super Cup against Barcelona in which he scored in the home leg. Who was he playing for?

a) Nottingham Forest   b) Aston Villa   c) Liverpool

10. In which Asian country did George play in 1981 – 82?

a) Japan   b) Hong Kong   c) Thailand

QUIZ 38: DAVID O'LEARY

1. **What position did O'Leary play?**

a) Central Defender   b) Centre Midfield   c) Forward

2. **Which international team did he represent?**

a) Northern Ireland   b) Republic of Ireland   c) Scotland

3. **What city was he born in?**

a) Dublin   b) London   c) Cardiff

4. **How old was O'Leary when he made his debut for Arsenal?**

a) 17   b) 18   c) 19

5. **What was his nickname?**

a) Dolly   b) Spider   c) Oily

6. **He made a record number of appearances for Arsenal. How many?**

a) 659   b) 691   c) 722

7. **How many seasons was O'Leary club captain?**

a) 3   b) 5   c) 7

8. **After he retired, he went into football management. Which team did he manage first?**

a) Leeds United   b) Aston Villa   c) Middlesbrough

9. **What was his highest finish in the Premiership as a manager?**

a) 2nd   b) 3rd   c) 4th

10. His last managerial role was in 2011 in which country?

a) India   b) China   c) United Arab Emirates

QUIZ 39: FREDDIE LJUNGBERG

1. **What was Ljungberg's first name?**

a) Fredrik   b) Karl   c) Sebastian

2. **At which Swedish club did he make his professional senior debut?**

a) Malmo   b) Halmstad   c) AIK

3. **Which other sport was he called up to the under 15 national team?**

a) Handball   b) Ice Hockey   c) Volleyball

4. **Freddie was signed in 1998 after Arsene Wenger had watched him on television against England playing for Sweden. He came off the bench and scored on his debut against which club?**

a) Chelsea   b) Manchester United   c) Liverpool

5. **Throughout his Arsenal career he struggled with injuries but which of these was a problem he suffered with?**

a) Blood Poisoning   b) Hyperextension   c) Gout

6. **How many seasons did he play for Arsenal?**

a) 7   b) 8   c) 9

7. **He made 325 appearances for the Gunners. How many goals did he score?**

a) 75   b) 88   c) 102

8. **After he left Arsenal, he played one more season in the Premier League for which club?**

a) Aston Villa   b) Newcastle United   c) West Ham United

9. Who was his first opponents on the 1st December 2019 as first team manager of Arsenal?

a) Norwich City   b) Crystal Palace   c) Bournemouth

10. He only managed one win as manager. Which team did they beat?

a) West Ham United   b) Everton   c) Southampton

QUIZ 40: NWANKWO KANU

1. Where was Nwankwo Kanu born?

a) Cameroon   b) Ghana   c) Nigeria

2. Kanu was captain of the Olympic team in 1996. What colour medal did he win?

a) Bronze   b) Silver   c) Gold

3. While having a medical in 1996 the doctors found a major problem, what was it?

a) Heart defect   b) Diabetes   c) Liver problem

4. From which team did he join Arsenal?

a) Ajax   b) Inter Milan   c) Bayern Munich

5. Which manager signed Kanu?

a) Arsene Wenger   b) Pat Rice   c) Stewart Houston

6. In 1999 at Stamford Bridge Kanu scored a hattrick saving Arsenal from a 2-0 deficit. How many minutes did it take him to compete his hattrick?

a) 17 minutes   b) 26 minutes   c) 35 minutes

7. He played 197 games for Arsenal, how many goals did he score?

a) 43   b) 63   c) 83

8. He left Arsenal before the 2004-05 season, which club did he join?

a) West Ham United   b) West Bromwich Albion   c) Portsmouth

9. In which English league did he finish his career?

a) Premier League   b) Championship   c) League one

10. How many times was he named African player of the year?

 a) 1   b) 2   c) 3

QUIZ 41: ALAN SMITH

1. Where in England was Alan Smith born?

a) Plumpton   b) Hollywood   c) Puddletown

2. Which club did Smith leave to join Arsenal?

a) Leicester City   b) Derby County   c) Nottingham Forest

3. Smith's first league goal came against Portsmouth on 29th August 1987. How many goals did he score in the game?

a) 1   b) 2   c) 3

4. In which season was Smith's best goal tally?

a) 1988-89   b) 1990-91   c) 1992-93

5. How many goals has Smith scored for Arsenal?

a) 115   b) 135   c) 155

6. How many first Division titles did he win with Arsenal?

a) 0   b) 1   c) 2

7. For which tournament did he make it into the England squad?

a) World Cup 1990   b) Euro 1992   c) World Cup 1994

8. In 1994 Arsenal won the European Cup Winners Cup thanks to an Alan Smith strike against which team to win 1 - 0?

a) Lazio   b) Sampdoria   c) Parma

9. **In 2011 Smith joined which TV company as a commentator?**
a) Sky TV   b) BBC   c) BT Sport

10. **Which computer game has used the commentary of Alan Smith along with Martin Tyler?**
a) Pro Evolution Soccer   b) FIFA   c) Championship Manager

QUIZ 42: FA CUP WINNERS 2014-15

1. **Arsenal beat Aston Villa in the 2015 final what was the score?**
a) 2-0   b) 3-0   c) 4-0

2. **Arsenal were the defending FA Cup winners in the 2015 final having won the 2014 final. Who did they defeat in the 2014 final?**
a) Hull City   b) Middlesbrough   c) Manchester United

3. **Who was the opposition manager in 2015?**
a) Roberto Di Matteo   b) Gerard Houllier   c) Tim Sherwood

4. **Which Championship side did Arsenal beat in the semi-final?**
a) Ipswich Town   b) Reading   c) Watford

5. **Arsenal won the semi-final 2 -1 after extra time. Who got both Arsenal goals?**
a) Alexis Sanchez   b) Mesut Ozil   c) Theo Walcott

6. **A children's TV program ran a competition to design a mascot for the final. Which TV program ran the competition?**
a) Newsround   b) FYI   c) Blue Peter

7. **Who was the Arsenal captain in the final?**
a) Laurent Koscielny   b) Santi Cazorla   c) Per Mertesacker

8. **Who was the only Englishman in the starting XI for Arsenal in the cup final?**
a) *Jack Wilshere*   b) *Theo Walcott*   c) *Alex Oxlade-Chamberlain*

9. **How many named substitutes were allowed in the final?**
a) *3*   b) *5*   c) *7*

10. **Who was voted the Man of the Match?**
a) *Alexis Sanchez*   b) *Santi Cazorla*   c) *Mesut Ozil*

QUIZ 43: FA CUP WINNERS 2019-20

1. **What was the official name of the FA Cup Final?**
a) *The Barclaycard Final*   b) *The 888 Final*   c) *The Heads Up Final*

2. **The football program was suspended in March. What stage of the FA Cup competition were the forthcoming games which were postponed??**
a) *Fifth Round*   b) *Quarter Finals*   c) *Semi Fianls*

3. **Arsenal won the final 2 – 1 against which team?**
a) *Manchester United*   b) *Tottenham Hotspurs*   c) *Chelsea*

4. **Who got the two goals for the Gunners?**
a) *Alexandre Lacazette*   b) *Pierre-Emerick Aubameyang*
c) *Granit Xhaka*

5. **Who did Arsenal beat in the semi final?**
a) *Manchester City*   b) *Manchester United*   c) *Everton*

6. **How many Frenchman were in the Arsenal squad?**
a) *0*   b) *1*   c) *2*

7. **Matteo Kovacic was sent off for Chelsea after receiving two yellow cards. How many players have been sent off in FA Cup finals?**

a) 4   *b)* 5   *c)* 6

8. **Who was the Arsenal goalkeeper in the final?**

a) *Bernd Leno*   *b)* *Emiliano Martinez*   *c)* *David Ospina*

9. **Where was Nicolas Pepe born?**

a) *France*   *b)* *Belgium*   *c)* *Ivory Coast*

10. **Who was man of the match in the 2020 final?**

a) *David Luiz*   *b)* *Granit Xhaka*   *c)* *Pierre-Emerick Aubameyang*

QUIZ 44: 'THE INVINCIBLES'

1. **In what season was Arsenal unbeaten and earned the name 'The Invincibles'?**

a) *2003-04*   *b)* *2004-05*   *c)* *2005-06*

2. **There have been two teams go unbeaten in the top flight of the football league. Who was the other team?**

a) *Everton*   *b)* *Preston North End*   *c)* *Wolverhampton Wanderers*

3. **What season was the unbeaten feat first achieved?**

a) *1888-89*   *b)* *1900-01*   *c)* *1905-06*

4. **How many games were there in the first ever invincible season?**

a) *22*   *b)* *26*   *c)* *30*

5. **Who was the Arsenal manager for the season?**

a) *George Graham*   *b)* *Pat Rice*   *c)* *Arsene Wenger*

6. **Before the season which goalkeeper left to join Manchester City on a free transfer?**

a) *Alex Manninger*   b) *David Seaman*   c) *John Lukic*

7. **Which keeper was signed as a replacement?**

a) *Jens Lehman*   b) *Manuel Almunia*   c) *Mart Poom*

8. **Although Arsenal went unbeaten all season in league matches, they lost their first preseason friendly to which club?**

a) *Barnet*   b) *Peterborough United*   c) *Cardiff City*

9. **Who did Arsenal beat on the opening weekend of the season?**

a) *Portsmouth*   b) *Charlton Athletic*   c) *Everton*

10. **Who was sent off for Arsenal in the opening league match?**

a) *Patrick Vieira*   b) *Sol Campbell*   c) *Ashley Cole*

QUIZ 45: 'THE INVINCIBLES' PART TWO

1. **Which outfield player played in 37 out of the 38 games?**

a) *Thierry Henry*   b) *Gilberto Silva*   c) *Kolo Toure*

2. **Thierry Henry finished top scorer for Arsenal in league matches but who finished second with 14 goals?**

a) *Jose Antonio Reyes*   b) *Freddie Ljungberg*   c) *Robert Pires*

3. **On 21st September Arsenal came extremely close to losing. They were down to ten men and conceded a last minute penalty to which team?**

a) *Chelsea*   b) *Manchester United*   c) *Liverpool*

4. **In November which player played for Leeds United against Arsenal after being given permission from Wenger as he was on loan from Arsenal?**

a) *Jermaine Pennant*   b) *Giovanni Van Bronckhorst*   c) *Moritz Volz*

5. How many games were left in the league season when Arsenal won the Premier League trophy?

 a) 2   b) 3   c) 4

6. At which ground did Arsenal win the league?

 a) Highbury   b) White Hart Lane   c) Stamford Bridge

7. How many games did Arsenal win in the season?

 a) 26   b) 30   c) 34

8. Which team finished second in the league this season?

 a) Liverpool   b) Chelsea   c) Manchester United

9. Arsenal hold the record for longest unbeaten run in the premiership. How many games was it?

 a) 45   b) 47   c) 49

10. Who ended the unbeaten run?

 a) Manchester United   b) Tottenham Hotspurs   c) Manchester City

QUIZ 46: PAT RICE

1. Which national team did Rice play for?

 a) Northern Ireland   b) Ireland   c) Scotland

2. At what age did he make his debut for Arsenal in a League Cup game against Burnley?

 a) 16   b) 18   c) 20

3. Which manager gave Pat his debut?

 a) Terry Neill   b) Billy Wright   c) Bertie Mee

4. Pat holds an Arsenal record with two other player of most FA Cup final appearances. How many finals did he play in?

 a) 3   b) 4   c) 5

5. **Who does he share the record with?**

a) Seaman and Parlour   b) Adams and Keown   c) Fabregas and Arteta

6. **As captain he led Arsenal to the final of the Cup Winners Cup in 1980 against Valencia. What was the result?**

a) Arsenal win   b) Shared trophy   c) Valencia win

7. **How many senior trophies did he win at Arsenal as a player?**

a) 2   b) 3   c) 4

8. **Rice left Arsenal at the end of the 1980 season to join which other London club?**

a) Watford   b) Crystal Palace   c) QPR

9. **Rice came back to Arsenal as youth team coach and later was assistant manager to Arsene Wenger. He spent four games as caretaker manager in which year?**

a) 1994   b) 1995   c) 1996

10. **Which honour was Rice given in the New Year's Honours in 2013?**

a) CBE   b) MBE   c) OBE

QUIZ 47: SOL CAMPBELL

1. **What is Sol's full first name?**

a) Soluwa   b) Saleem   c) Sulzeer

2. **He started his career in the West Ham United youth system playing what position?**

a) Right Back   b) Central Midfield   c) Striker

3. **At which club did he spend most of his playing career?**

a) Arsenal   b) Tottenham Hotspur   c) Newcastle United

4. **Which season was Sol's first as an Arsenal player?**
a) *2000-01*   b) *2001-02*   c) *2002-03*

5. **How many trophies did Sol win in his first season as an Arsenal player?**
a) *0*   b) *1*   c) *2*

6. **In the 2003-04, the 'Invincible' season, who was Sol's central defender partner in most games?**
a) *Kolo Toure*   b) *Martin Keown*   c) *Pascal Cygan*

7. **Arsenal managed to get to the Champions League final in 2006 thanks to an impressive defensive record. They went 10 consecutive matches without conceding. In the final Sol scored the opening goal but Arsenal went on to lose 2-1 to which team?**
a) *Real Madrid*   b) *Barcelona*   c) *Atletico Madrid*

8. **At which world cup was Sol named in the team of the tournament despite England been knocked out in the quarter finals?**
a) *1998*   b) *2002*   c) *2006*

9. **Which club did Sol join after leaving Arsenal in 2006?**
a) *Portsmouth*   b) *Newcastle United*   c) *Notts County*

10. **Which English league club side was Sol's first as manager?**
a) *Southend United*   b) *Oldham Athletic*   c) *Macclesfield Town*

QUIZ 48: RAY PARLOUR

1. **What was Ray's nickname?**
a) *The Romford Maradona*   b) *The Romford Puskas*   c) *The Romford Pele*

2. How many appearances did he make for Arsenal?

a) 366   b) 466   c) 566

3. Ray made his senior debut for Arsenal against Liverpool. Which of the following did he do on debut?

a) Concede a penalty   b) Get sent off   c) Score an own goal

4. In what year did he make his debut?

a) 1990   b) 1992   c) 1994

5. Which manager gave him his senior debut?

a) George Graham   b) Bruce Rioch   c) Arsene Wenger

6. In 2000 Ray was part of the Arsenal team that reached the final of the UEFA Cup. The final went to penalties, and he was the only one of the Arsenal players to score. Who were the opposition?

a) Porto   b) Monaco   c) Galatasaray

7. After leaving Arsenal which club did he join to continue his career?

a) Middlesbrough   b) Hull City   c) Barnsley

8. How many trophies did Parlour win at Arsenal?

a) 8   b) 10   c) 12

9. How many goals did he net for Arsenal?

a) 32   b) 53   c) 74

10. In June 2012 Ray came out of retirement, along with several others, to play for which team in the FA Cup?

a) Romford FC   b) Wembley   c) Barking FC

QUIZ 49: CHARITY/COMMUNITY SHIELD

1. Who did Arsenal beat in the 2020 FA Community Shield?

a) Liverpool   b) Chelsea   c) Manchester City

2. Who did Arsenal beat in the 2017 FA Community Shield?

a) Manchester United   b) Chelsea   c) Southampton

3. Who did Arsenal beat in the 2015 FA Community Shield?

a) Chelsea   b) Everton   c) Tottenham Hotspur

4. Who did Arsenal beat in the 2014 FA Community Shield?

a) Manchester City   b) Leicester City   c) Chelsea

5. Who did Arsenal beat in the 2004 FA Community Shield?

a) Manchester United   b) Liverpool   c) Blackburn Rovers

6. Who did Arsenal beat in the 2002 FA Community Shield?

a) Chelsea   b) Liverpool   c) West Ham United

7. Who did Arsenal beat in the 1999 FA Charity Shield?

a) Blackburn Rovers   b) Newcastle United   c) Manchester United

8. Who did Arsenal beat in the 1998 FA Charity Shield?

a) Middlesbrough   b) Manchester United   c) Chelsea

9. Who did Arsenal share the trophy with in the 1991 FA Charity Shield?

a) Nottingham Forest   b) Tottenham Hotspur   c) Everton

10. Who did Arsenal beat in the 1951 FA Charity Shield?

a) Preston North End   b) Bolton Wanderers   c) Blackpool

Quiz 50: Miscellaneous

1. **After Manchester United defeated Arsenal to end their unbeaten run there was a scuffle in the tunnel after. What was the name given to this?**
   a) *Sour Grapes*   b) *Pizzagate*   c) *The Keane Vieira Dance*

2. **Which club did Mesut Ozil play for before joining Arsenal?**
   a) *Borussia Dortmund*   b) *Bayern Munich*   c) *Real Madrid*

3. **Which player was given the nickname 'Baby Kanu'?**
   a) *Emmanuel Adebayor*   b) *Pierre-Emerick Aubameyang*
   c) *Sylvain Wiltord*

4. **From which club did Arsenal sign Alexandre Lacazette?**
   a) *Monaco*   b) *PSG*   c) *Lyon*

5. **Which Arsenal caretaker manager has a credit for co-writing Chelsea's 'Blue is the colour'?**
   a) *Stewart Houston*   b) *Pat Rice*   c) *Steve Burtenshaw*

6. **Which Arsenal player scored the last goal at Highbury?**
   a) *Robert Pires*   b) *Thierry Henry*   c) *Freddie Ljungberg*

7. **Which company was the kit manufacturer when Arsenal won the league in the 2003-04 season?**
   a) *Puma*   b) *Adidas*   c) *Nike*

8. **And who was the main shirt sponsor in the 2003-04 season?**
   a) *O2*   b) *JVC*   c) *Fly Emirates*

9. **What was different about the trophy they were awarded for the invincible season?**
   a) *It was twice the size*   b) *It was gold*   c) *It had four handles*

10. **What was special about Arsenal's match against Sheffield United on 22nd January 1927?**

a) *It was the first time Arsenal wore red before the end as they ran out of balls*   b) *The game was abandoned*   c) *It was the first game to be broadcast live on the radio*

11. **Arsenal hold the record for the highest number of players from a single club in an England team. It was England versus Italy in a friendly in 1934. How many players were from Arsenal?**

a) *5*   b) *7*   c) *9*

12. **Which Arsenal player was the first to be red carded at The Emirates?**

a) *Phillipe Senderos*   b) *Kolo Toure*   c) *Abou Diaby*

13. **Arsenal's first Premier League game was a loss to which team?**

a) *Norwich City*   b) *Ipswich Town*   c) *Leeds United*

14. **Cliff Bastin played 396 games for the Gunners scoring how many goals?**

a) *143*   b) *159*   c) *178*

15. **How much did Arsenal sell Adebayor to Manchester City for?**

a) *£20 million*   b) *£25 million*   c) *£30 million*

16. **What year was the last time Arsenal weren't in the top tier of English football?**

a) *1915*   b) *1935*   c) *1955*

17. **In the season 2017-18 Arsenal only received one red card in all competitions. Who received the red card?**

a) *Mathieu Debuchy*   b) *Dinos Mavropanos*   c) *Chuba Akpom*

18. **Which player left Manchester United to join Arsenal in 2014?**

a) *Danny Welbeck*   b) *Calum Chambers*   c) *Alexis Sanchez*

19. Ashley Cole married which Girls Aloud member?

a) *Nicola*   b) *Sarah*   c) *Cheryl*

20. Where is Arsenal's training ground located?

a) *Shenley*   b) *Boreham Wood*   c) *Wimbledon*

21. In which stadium was the 2006 Champions league final held, where Arsenal lost to Barcelona?

a) *San Siro*   b) *Stade De France*   c) *Millennium Stadium*

22. Which former player was named as technical director in 2019?

a) *Edu*   b) *Patrick Vieira*   c) *Dennis Bergkamp*

23. What position does Lord Harris of Peckham hold in 2020?

a) *Contract Negotiator*   b) *Chief Executive Officer*   c) *Director*

24. What nationality is Tomas Rosicky?

a) *Russian*   b) *Czech*   c) *Polish*

25. Since the beginning of the football league who has won more head to head matches?

a) *Arsenal*   b) *Draw*   c) *Tottenham Hotspur*

26. In 2011-12 season who did Arsenal lose 8-2 against?

a) *Liverpool*   b) *Manchester City*   c) *Manchester City*

27. In the same 2011-12 season who did Arsenal beat 7-1?

a) *Blackburn Rovers*   b) *Wigan Athletic*   c) *Swansea City*

28. Manchester United won the 1999 – 00 Premier League from Arsenal by how many points.

a) *14 points*   b) *16 points*   c) *18 points*

29. John Radford, one of Arsenal's greats, was born in what county?

a) *Kent*   b) *Yorkshire*   c) *Norwich*

30. Who did David O'Leary say the following about 'I remember thinking he must be some player to wear those white boots'?

a) *Charlie Nicholas*   *b) Alan Ball*   *c) Liam Brady*

31. How many appearances did Frank Stapleton make for the Gunners?

a) *250*   *b) 275*   *c) 300*

32. Ted Drake is the highest scorer for Arsenal in a single match. How many did he score against Aston Villa in December 1935?

a) *7*   *b) 8*   *c) 9*

33. How many times have Arsenal done the League and FA Cup double?

a) *1*   *b) 2*   *c) 3*

34. What was unique about Arsenal's match against Manchester United on 31st January 2010?

a) *First match in 3D*   *b) First match in HD*   *c) First match in 4K*

35. What nationality is goalkeeper Alex Manninger?

a) *French*   *b) Austrian*   *c) German*

36. In 2019 Arsenal reached the final of the Europa League. Who were there opponents?

a) *Sevilla*   *b) Borussia Dortmund*   *c) Chelsea*

37. Arsenal lost the Europa League final. What was the score?

a) *4-1*   *b) 2-0*   *c) 3-2*

38. What country was the final held in?

a) *Azerbaijan*   *b) Romania*   *c) Poland*

39. Who scored the goal against Manchester United that clinched the double in 2002?

a) *Thierry Henry*   *b) Robert Pires*   *c) Sylvain Wiltord*

40. Which Arsenal player earnt England caps both in football and cricket?

a) Denis Compton   b) Andy Ducat   c) Alex James

41. Which Arsenal player has been sent off the most times in Premier League games?

a) Martin Keown   b) Patrick Vieira   c) Granit Xhaka

42. What team did Arsenal sign Thomas Partey from?

a) Marseille   b) Atletico Madrid   c) Juventus

43. What position did Kenny Sansom play most of his career in?

a) Full Back   b) Central Midfield   c)Left Wing

44. Which player did Arsene Wenger sign at Monaco and then again at Arsenal?

a) Robert Pires   b) Emmanuel Petit   c) Sylvain Wiltord

45. How many appearances did Nigel Winterburn make for Arsenal?

a) 457   b) 516   c) 584

46. What nationality is Alexis Sanchez?

a) Colombian   b) Peruvian   c) Chilian

47. Who was the only Arsenal player in the England World Cup winning squad of 1966?

a) George Armstrong   b) George Eastham   c) Jon Radford

48. How is Peter Lovell connected to the club?

a) First million pound signing   b) Designed the clubs mascot
c) The architect of The Emirates

49. Arsenal hold the record for most FA Cup trophies. How many have they won?

a) 12   b) 14   c) 16

50. In 2003-04 Arsenal went unbeaten all season in the Premier League. Can you name the 11 players who made the most

appearances in Premier League games for the club that season?

QUOTATIONS – WHO SAID IT?

1. When you give success to stupid people, it makes them more stupid sometimes and not more intelligent.

2. What does Arsenal mean? It means class. The structure of the Club, everything has a classy feel about it. It isn't always about success, there is more than that and this is what makes it a cut above the rest.

3. Have Tottenham closed the gap on Arsenal? Last time I checked they were still 4 miles and 11 titles away.

4. Everyone thinks they have the prettiest wife at home.

5. I liked a fight and always stood up for myself. That's how I was brought up. Coming from Holloway you learn from the pram to nut people that pick on you.

6. We didn't think he would play on Sunday because he was suspended - that makes me think he has all the qualities to join Arsenal.

7. When people think Arsenal had a bad season and we've had a good one, yet they still finish above us, it hurts.

8. So here, at Arsenal, we are often surprised when we are shown some of the newspapers, and at the bottom of an article there is a line saying if you know of anyone who had an affair with a player, call this number. It is very strange to us.

9. I knew before I came to Arsenal what kind of players were here. And of course, in training, you can see how many good players are here; the most important thing is that we work well as a team - that's the most important thing.

10. I have to admit I love banners like 'We don't need Batman, we've got Robin' and stuff like that.

11. There's only one person gets you sacked and that's the fans.

12. There's still 45 minutes to go - for both sides, I would guess.

13. The ref was booking so many I thought he was filling his lotto numbers.

14. The way Arsenal are passing the ball is as if they are telepathetic.

15. I tried to watch the Tottenham match on television in my hotel yesterday, but I fell asleep.

16. I'd compare myself to Zinedine Zidane – a humble guy who just happened to be the best.

17. Without being too harsh on David Beckham, he cost us the match.

18. I've been consistent in patches this season.

19. It took a lot of bottle for Tony to own up.

20. It's all very well batting from the same hymn sheet.

21. I don't want Rooney to leave these shores but if he does, I think he'll go abroad.

22. Football's all about yesterday, it's all about now.

23. If you said as much as "how are you" to him (Rosicky), he would then be injured for two and a half months.

24. Tony Fernandes is in that goldfish bowl and he's swimming against the tide.

25. Is Dreamcast the name of the team?

26. I've got passion but no idea of tactics. I'd be like a black Kevin Keegan.

27. When I first put him at centre forward, he said, 'Look I cannot score goals'. For someone who cannot score goals he has done quite well.

28. Play for the name on the front of the shirt, and they'll remember the name on the back.

29. After five minutes I knew how good he was because Bergkamp kept giving him the ball.

30. In football, yeah, sometimes you get these multitalented individuals where that's all they want to do: when the team's got the ball, I'll play but, when we haven't got the ball, I'll go and have a rest.

31. I realised when I joined Arsenal that the back four were all University Graduates in the art of defending and Tony Adams was the Doctor of Defence.

32. I was a scorer of great goals. Great own goals.

33. If you were constructing a team of nice people, David Rocastle would be captain.

34. It sticks in the craw because nobody likes the Arsenal, but you simply can't help but enjoy watching the football they play.

35. I think we can go a whole season unbeaten.

36. If you eat caviar every day it's difficult to return to sausages.

37. I was a young lad when I was growing up.

38. Fergie said I was a Manchester United player in the wrong shirt – I said he was an Arsenal manager in the wrong blazer.

39. Sometimes I am the 'philosophical professor', or I can do the voice like thunder if necessary... or if I want to keep the lads on their toes I might sit back and give them a thousand-yard stare.

40. Sometimes in football, you have to score goals.

41. A contract on a piece of paper, saying you want to leave, is like a piece of paper saying you want to leave.

42. What's it like being in Bethlehem, the place where Christmas began? I suppose it's like seeing Ian Wright at Arsenal.

43. They've literally got no players left - and then with 95 minutes gone they score.

44. Thierry Henry, when he came, was literally like a fish up a tree.

45. I'm not a believer in luck, but I do believe you need it.

46. They (Leeds United) used to be a bit like Arsenal, winning by one goal to nil or even less.

47. I don't want to be either partial or impartial.

48. Robinho has been literally non-existent.

49. It seems that they're playing with one leg tied together.

50. Its one nil to the Arsenal. That's the way we like it.

Answers

Quiz 1: The Start Answers

1. 1886
2. Dial Square, later became known as Royal Arsenal then Woolwich Arsenal before just Arsenal
3. Nottingham Forest
4. 1893. They had tried to start a football league south but failed. They were the first London club to play in the football league.
5. Fulham
6. Tottenham Hotspur. In the season Arsenal finished sixth behind Tottenham, but as they were expanding the First Division they voted to promote Arsenal instead
7. FA Cup in 1930
8. They finished ninth
9. 1913
10. 1913

Quiz 2: Arsene Wenger Answers

1. Charles Earnest
2. Strasbourg
3. Japan at Nagoya Grampus Eight
4. He was appointed 1st October 1996
5. He won the FA Cup 7 times and runner up once
6. Bruce Rioch. Pat Rice and Stewart Houston were both caretakers prior to Wenger's arrival
7. Blackburn Rovers and the score was a 2-0 win
8. 17 trophies – 7 FA Cups, 3 League titles and 7 Charity/Community Shields
9. 2018
10. The score in his last game was a 1-0 win a Huddersfield

Quiz 3: George Graham Answers

1. George was born on 30th November 1944
2. Manchester United
3. £50,000 plus player Tommy Baldwin
4. He signed for California Surf in the USA
5. He played for Scotland 12 times
6. 1986
7. Millwall
8. 4th
9. They scored a total of 40 goals and finished 10th in the league
10. It was an unsolicited gift. He accepted a payment of £425,000 from a Norwegian agent for the signing of two players

Quiz 4: Terry Neill answers

1. He is Northern Irish
2. 28 years old. One of the youngest managers ever
3. He was player manager at Hull City
4. William John Terence Neill is his full name
5. Tottenham Hotspur
6. He replaced Bertie Mee
7. 1978/79 they beat Manchester United 3-2
8. Valencia
9. They lost on penalties at the Heysel Stadium
10. Charlie Nicholas from Celtic

Quiz 5: Bertie Mee Answers

1. He received the OBE in 1984 for services to football
2. Physio
3. The city had to hold a trade fair to qualify
4. UEFA Cup
5. 4-3 they lost first leg 3-1 away and won the home leg 3-0

6. Liverpool 2-1 after extra time
7. Tottenham Hotspur in 1961
8. 11 years
9. Watford. He was assistant to Graham Taylor
10. Arsene Wenger

QUIZ 6: UNAI EMERY ANSWERS

1. He left PSG
2. He is Spanish
3. Arsenal lost 0-2
4. They beat West Ham United at home 3-1
5. He won 55% of his games
6. Sevilla won the Europa League 2013/14, 2014/15 and 2015/16
7. They lost to Chelsea 4-1
8. Nicolas Pepe for £72million
9. 4 years at Valencia
10. Eintracht Frankfurt, they lost 2-1

QUIZ 7: MIKEL ARTETA ANSWERS

1. 1982
2. He signed for Rangers in 2002
3. He is Spanish
4. 2011
5. He played for Everton before Arsenal
6. £10 million on a 4 year contract
7. He scored 14 goals
8. He had 110 appearances
9. He was the assistant manager at Manchester City
10. His first game as manager was on 26th December 2019 against Bournemouth, it finished 1-1.

Quiz 8: Charlie Nicholas Answers

1. He was a striker
2. Celtic
3. 1983
4. Switzerland
5. Terry Neill signed him before getting the sack a few months later
6. 1983
7. They paid £750,000
8. He didn't score again until Boxing Day in December
9. He scored a penalty against Birmingham in a 1-1 draw
10. Champagne after his London lifestyle

Quiz 9: Pat Jennings Answers

1. He was awarded an OBE
2. Gaelic Football
3. Watford
4. Wales
5. It was from Tottenham where he was for 13 years
6. He was PFA Player of the Year. Jennings and Shilton are the only keepers to win the award
7. 8 Years
8. He won 1 FA Cup and lost 3 other competition finals
9. His last game was against Brazil in the 1986 World Cup at 41 Years Old
10. 2003

Quiz 10: Thierry Henry Answers

1. Daniel
2. His first club was Monaco
3. They signed him from Juventus

4. He was bought for £11 million
5. He scored a total of 228 goals
6. It took until the third season to win silverware
7. Ian Wright held the record
8. He scored 39 goals
9. He played for New York Red Bulls
10. His first head managerial role was at Monaco

QUIZ 11: DENNIS BERGKAMP ANSWERS

1. He is Dutch
2. He had a phobia of flying and was nicknamed 'the non-flying Dutchman'
3. 1995
4. Denis Law, they added an 'n' to differentiate from Denise
5. 1986
6. They signed him from Inter Milan
7. Bruce Rioch signed Bergkamp
8. Oxford United
9. Ajax
10. August 1997

QUIZ 12: TONY ADAMS ANSWERS

1. He was born in Romford
2. 1, his only club was Arsenal
3. 17 years old
4. Terry Neill gave him his debut a month before he was sacked
5. He made 672 appearances
6. He won 4 titles, 2 Premier Leagues and 2 First Division
7. He was appointed the manager at Wycombe Wanderers
8. He won 16 games as a manager

9. His autobiography was titled Addicted making links to his alcoholism. Tom Sheen of the Guardian Newspaper called him a stopper.
10. In 2019 he became president of the Rugby Football League

QUIZ 13: IAN WRIGHT ANSWERS

1. His first professional club was Crystal Palace
2. Arsenal paid £2.5 million
3. He scored 3 against Southampton in his first game for Arsenal. He also played Southampton last game of the season where he got another 3.
4. 29 league goals
5. Bruce Rioch
6. He played for Celtic
7. He was awarded the MBE
8. He scored a total of 185 goals
9. They both played for Manchester City
10. Nike used the slogan on billboards

QUIZ 14: THE EMIRATES ANSWERS

1. It is 450m away from Highbury
2. £0. It was all self-funded although Wenger said lots of other stadiums around the world were built by governments. An example being Bayern Munich who paid 1 Euro for their ground
3. The record attendance is 60,161 for a Premier League match against Manchester United on the 3rd November 2007
4. The first competitive match was against Aston Villa
5. Olof Mellberg scored the first goal at the Emirates
6. Brazil have played 8 friendlies there winning 7 of them
7. The playing area measures 105m x 68m
8. Nicolas Sarkozy, the French president, met Gordon Brown
9. 7-0 against Slavia Prague in the Champions League in 2007

10. The total cost was £390 million

Quiz 15: Highbury

1. 1913
2. They were not allowed to sell alcohol or play on Holy days
3. It cost £125,000
4. 73,295 vs Sunderland in 1935
5. Belgium in 1923
6. They had to use White Hart Lane
7. Muhammad Ali
8. East Stand
9. Highbury Square
10. They played 2010, winning 1196, drawing 475 and losing 339

Quiz 16: 1960's Transfer Answers

1. Newcastle United
2. Tommy Docherty
3. Torino
4. Goalkeeper
5. Frank McLintock
6. 1 season and was sold to Sheffield United
7. George Graham
8. Coventry City
9. £80,000
10. Bob Wilson

Quiz 17: 1970's Transfer Answers

1. Hibernian
2. Martin Peters
3. Manchester United
4. 0 he kept a clean sheet

5. Manchester United
6. £200,000
7. Northern Ireland
8. Wolverhampton Wanderers
9. Brian Talbot
10. He was sold to Seattle Sounders

QUIZ 18: 1980'S TRANSFER ANSWERS

1. Clive Allen
2. Crystal Palace
3. £900,000
4. Charlie Nicholas
5. Manchester City
6. Brighton & Hove Albion
7. Viv Anderson
8. 1988
9. Brian Marwood
10. Stoke City

QUIZ 19: 1990'S TRANSFER ANSWERS

1. Manchester City
2. David Seaman
3. Andy Cole
4. He arrived from Inter Milan
5. £7.5 million
6. Sampdoria
7. 1996
8. 1997
9. West Ham United
10. Juventus

Quiz 20: 2000's Transfers Answers

1. He was bought from Mallorca
2. 287 appearances
3. Free
4. Barcelona
5. West Bromwich Albion
6. 16. He signed as a scholar until his 17th birthday and then signed a professional contract
7. Juventus
8. William Gallas
9. Cardiff
10. £25 million

Quiz 21: 2010's Transfers Answers

1. Notts County
2. Werder Bremen
3. Barnsley
4. £42.5 million
5. Barcelona
6. He plays for and has captained Switzerland
7. Galatasary
8. Borussia Dortmund
9. Athletico Madrid had a two transfer window ban upheld
10. £72 million

Quiz 22: First Division Winners 1952–53 Answers

1. Arsenal lost 9 games on their way to winning the league
2. The deciding factor was goal ratio. This was the number of goals scored divided by the number conceded. Arsenals ratio

was 1.516. It was 0.099 better than second placed team. This system was scrapped in the 1976 – 77 season

3. Doug Lishman with 22 goals
4. Liverpool
5. Preston North End were the unlucky team to finish runners up
6. It was their 7th league title
7. They beat Blackpool 3-1
8. Ray Daniel
9. Tom Whittaker
10. They lost to Blackpool 2 - 1

QUIZ 23: INTER CITIES FAIRS CUP WINNERS 1969-70

1. The defending champions were Newcastle United
2. It was Jon Sammels who scored 6 goals in the competition
3. Anderlecht
4. 4-3 they lost 3-1 away and won 3-0 at home
5. Frank McLintock was captain
6. It was substitute Ray Kennedy. Substitutes weren't allowed in the second leg in England
7. Bertie Mee
8. Ajax
9. FC Koln beat Arsenal 2-2 on away goals
10. They are from Romania

QUIZ 24: FA CUP 1970-71 ANSWERS

1. It was Liverpool
2. Bertie Mee
3. It was Chelsea
4. It was Eddie Kelly
5. Charlie George scored in the 111th minute
6. It was Tottenham in 1960-61
7. Bob Wilson
8. They beat Stoke City 2-0 in the replay after drawing 2-2

9. It was Ray Kennedy
10. There were 3, Bob Wilson, George Graham and Frank McLintock

QUIZ 25: FIRST DIVISION WINNERS 1970-71 ANSWERS

1. Leeds United
2. Stoke City 5-0
3. Liverpool
4. 25 clean sheets
5. Ron Davies
6. Ray Kennedy in a 1-0 win
7. West Bromwich Albion
8. Leeds United they drew 0-0 at home and lost 1-0 away
9. They reached the quarter finals
10. Ajax knocked them out

QUIZ 26: FA CUP WINNERS 1978-79 ANSWERS

1. It took 5 games to get a winner. The scores were 1-1, 1-1, 2-2, 3-3 and 2-0
2. Sheffield Wednesday
3. 11 matches
4. Frank Stapleton and Alan Sunderland with 6 each
5. Wolverhampton Wanderers
6. Villa Park
7. Terry Neill. It was his only trophy as manager
8. Manchester United
9. Alan Sunderland
10. It was nicknamed the 5 minute final as Arsenal were cruising 2-0 until Manchester United scored in the 86th and 88th minute and then Arsenal got the winner in the 89th.

Quiz 27: First Division Winners 1988-89 Answers

1. ITV brought the rights for £11million up from the previous £5.2million
2. Arsenal won 4-0
3. Beat Bayern Munich to win on goal difference
4. Liverpool
5. Wimbledon
6. Alan Smith with 25 league goals
7. 5-0
8. Tony Adams
9. Arsenal won on goals scored after Thomas' last minute goal ensured they were level on points and goal difference
10. It was the Hillsborough disaster. Arsenal were not allowed to enter the European Cup as a ban from UEFA was still in force from the Heysel disaster

Quiz 28: FA Cup Winners 1992-93

1. It was Sheffield Wednesday
2. Arsenal and Sheffield met in the league cup final where Arsenal won 2-1
3. It was David O'Leary who left for Leeds after 722 games
4. The rules for replays were changed from 1999 and this was the last one decided by a replay
5. It was Andy Linighan
6. He got his one and only yellow card
7. He is Danish
8. They beat Tottenham 1-0
9. It was Ian Wright who got 10 FA Cup goals this season
10. George Graham

Quiz 29: Premier League Winners 2001-02
Answers

1. Their shirt sponsor was Dreamcast
2. They lost 0, they drew 5 and won 14
3. Freddie Ljungberg
4. Liverpool
5. 6
6. Aliadiere, Grimandi, Henry, Pires, Vieira and Wiltord
7. Ray Parlour, the others were sent off twice
8. Lee Dixon 616 appearances and Tony Adams 672 appearances
9. FA Cup
10. They beat Manchester United 1-0

Quiz 30: FA Cup 2002 - 03 Answers

1. Robert Pires scored in the 31st minute
2. It was the Gunners having beaten Chelsea 2 – 0 in the previous years final
3. Gordon Strachan
4. It was played at the Millenium Stadium during the rebuilding of Wembley
5. It was Lauren
6. It was David Seaman. The regular captain, Parick Vieira was injured and Sol Campbell suspended
7. It was David Seaman again
8. Thierry Henry
9. It was Man Utd
10. He won it 7 times – 1997 – 98, 2001 – 02, 2002 – 03, 2004 – 05, 2014 – 15 and 2016 - 17

Quiz 31: Club Captains Answers

1. Frank McLintock
2. Pat Rice
3. Graham Rix
4. Tony Adams
5. Patrick Vieira
6. Cesc Fabregas
7. Robin van Persie
8. Mikel Arteta
9. Per Mertesacker
10. Laurent Koscielny

Quiz 32: Player Of The Season Answers

1. Thierry Henry
2. Cesc Fabregas
3. Robin van Persie
4. Jack Wilshere
5. Santi Cazorla
6. Aaron Ramsey
7. Alexis Sanchez
8. Mesut Ozil
9. Alexandre Lacazette
10. Pierre-Emerick Aubameyang

Quiz 33: Patrick Vieira Answers

1. He was born in Dakar, Senegal
2. It was Cannes
3. AC Milan
4. Bruce Rioch was sacked two days before he signed and it was Stewart Houston who was caretaker manager when he signed
5. He scored 33 goals

6. They beat Brazil 3-0 with Vieira coming on as a substitute
7. He played 107 games for France scoring 6 goals
8. He signed for Juventus
9. It was Manchester City
10. He won 9 – Premier League in 1997 – 98, 2001 – 02 and 2003 – 04. FA Cup in 1997 – 98, 2001 – 02 and 2004 – 05. The Charity Shield in 1998, 1999 and 2002

QUIZ 34: DAVID SEAMAN ANSWERS

1. He was born in Rotherham on the 19th September 1963
2. Leeds
3. He cost Peterborough £4,000
4. It was George Graham who beat the British record for a goalkeeper paying £1.3m
5. Arsenal conceded 18 goals
6. He played 75 games
7. It was Manchester City
8. He made 564 appearances for Arsenal
9. Safe Hands
10. He took to the skates on Dancing on Ice

QUIZ 35: LIAM BRADY ANSWERS

1. He was born in Dublin
2. He made his debut on the 6th October 1973 and Bertie Mee was manager
3. 1979
4. He played 307 games for Arsenal
5. He scored 59 goals
6. He won 1 trophy the 1979 FA Cup
7. He signed for Juventus
8. In 1987 he signed for West Ham United
9. It was Celtic
10. Chippy

QUIZ 36: ROBERT PIRES ANSWERS

1. Metz
2. It was Marseille
3. There were 5 – Robert Pires, Thierry Henry, Sylvain Wiltord, Patrick Vieira and Gilles Grimandi
4. It was in an FA Cup game against Newcastle
5. It was Jermaine Pennant
6. He was substituted in the 18th minute following the sending off of goalkeeper Jens Lehman. This was one of the factors that made him feel he was no longer a valued first team player and leave the club
7. They beat Italy 2-1 aet
8. He joined Villareal
9. He played 79 times for France
10. In July 2014 Pires played for Goa to help launch the Indian Premier League. He eventually retired on the 25th February 2016 aged 42

QUIZ 37: CHARLIE GEORGE ANSWERS

1. He is Charles Frederick George
2. He played 179 games and scored 49 times
3. They beat Liverpool 2 – 1
4. Derby County
5. It was Real Madrid
6. The Minnesota Kicks
7. On the 8th September 1976 he played his only game for England against the Republic of Ireland
8. He lost a finger in a lawn mower accident
9. He was playing for Nottingham Forest
10. He played for Bulova which played in the Hong Kong League

Quiz 38: David O'Leary Answers

1. Central Defender
2. Republic of Ireland
3. Born in London and moved to Dublin when he was 4 years old
4. He made his debut at 17 and made 30 appearances that season
5. His nickname was Spider
6. He made 722 appearances in all competitions
7. It was 3 in the season between 1980 and 1983
8. Leeds United
9. He managed a third place finish in the 1999-2000 season with Leeds
10. Shabab Al-Ahli in the United Arab Emirates

Quiz 39: Freddie Ljungberg Answers

1. He is Karl Fredrik Ljungberg
2. He played for Halmstad
3. He played for Sweden under 15s in handball although he was also keen on ice hockey
4. Manchester United in a 3-0 win
5. Blood Poisoning from his large tattoos
6. 9 seasons 1998-2007
7. 75 goals
8. West Ham United
9. Norwich in a 2-2 draw
10. West Ham United 3-1

Quiz 40: Nwankwo Kanu Answers

1. He was born in Nigeria
2. He won the gold medal

3. Heart Defect – He had surgery to replace his aortic valve and afterwards set up the Kanu Heart Foundation to help young African children with heart defects
4. He played for Inter Milan
5. Arsene Wenger
6. It was a 17 minute hattrick
7. 43 goals
8. It was West Bromwich Albion
9. It was in the Championship with Portsmouth
10. He won it twice, 1996 and 1999

QUIZ 41: ALAN SMITH ANSWERS

1. He was born in Hollywood
2. He left Leicester City
3. 3 goals
4. 1990-91
5. 115 goals
6. 2 1988-89 and 1990-91
7. European Championships 1992
8. They beat Parma
9. Sky TV
10. FIFA – from FIFA 12 through to FIFA 20

QUIZ 42: FA CUP WINNERS 2014-15 ANSWERS

1. The score was 4-0 to Arsenal
2. They beat Hull 3-2 after extra time
3. It was Tim Sherwood
4. Reading
5. Alexis Sanchez got the goals

6. It was Blue Peter. The winning entry was 'Billie' which was based on the horse which helped to clear the pitch before the 1923 final
7. Per Mertesacker
8. It was Theo Walcott. Wilshere and Oxlade-Chamberlain were on the bench
9. There were 7 named substitutes allowed
10. Santi Cazorla

QUIZ 43: FA CUP WINNERS 2019-20 ANSWERS

1. It was known as the Heads Up Final which was part of a campaign on mental health
2. The quarter final was the round where the delay occurred
3. Chelsea
4. Pierre – Emerick Aubameyang got both goals
5. They beat Man City 2 – 0
6. There was only one Alexandre Lacazette
7. There have been 6 – Kevin Moran (1985), Jose Antonio Reyes (2005), Pablo Zabaleta (2013), Chris Smalling (2016), Victor Moses (2016) and Matteo Kovacic (2020)
8. Emiliano Martinez
9. He was born in France but plays for the Ivory Coast
10. Pierre-Emerick Aubameyang

QUIZ 44: 'THE INVINCIBLES' ANSWERS

1. 2003-04
2. Preston North End were the other invincibles
3. They did it in 1888-89 the founding year of the new football league
4. Only 12 teams in the league so only 22 games
5. Arsene Wenger
6. It was David Seaman
7. They got Jens Lehman from Borussia Dortmund

8. It was a 1-0 loss to Peterborough
9. Everton 2-1
10. Sol Campbell was sent off for a professional foul

QUIZ 45: 'THE INVINCIBLES' PART TWO ANSWERS

1. Thierry Henry
2. Robert Pires
3. It was Manchester United with a penalty missed by Ruud Van Nistelrooy
4. It was Jermaine Pennant
5. 4 games were left
6. White Hart Lane
7. They won 26 and drew 12
8. Chelsea finished second 11 points behind
9. 49 games
10. Manchester United beat Arsenal 2-0

QUIZ 46: PAT RICE ANSWERS

1. Northern Ireland
2. 18 years old
3. Bertie Mee in 1967
4. 5 FA Cup finals
5. It was Seaman and Parlour
6. Valencia won on penalties
7. He won 3 trophies – First Division winners 1970-71 and FA Cup 1971 and 1979
8. He joined Watford
9. It was 1996 just before Arsene Wenger was appointed
10. He got an MBE

Quiz 47: 2nd Sol Campbell Answers

1. His first name is Sulzeer
2. He began as a striker
3. Tottenham Hotspur
4. He joined for the 2001-02 season
5. 2 trophies – Premier League and FA Cup
6. He partnered Kolo Toure the most
7. It was Barcelona
8. 2002 world cup in South Korea and Japan. They lost to Brazil in the quarter finals
9. He joined Portsmouth
10. He managed Macclesfield Town

Quiz 48: Ray Parlour Answers

1. He was nicknamed 'The Romford Pele'
2. 466 appearances
3. He conceded a penalty
4. He made his debut in 1992
5. George Graham was the manager
6. They lost to Galatasary
7. He joined Middlesbrough then Hull City
8. He won a massive 12 trophies – Premier league 97-98, 2001-02,03-04 FA Cup 92-93, 97-98, 2001-02, 02-03 League Cup 92-93 Community Shield 98, 99, 2002 UEFA Cup Winners Cup 93-94
9. He scored 32 goals
10. He played for Wembley

Quiz 49: Charity/Community Shield Answers

1. Arsenal beat Liverpool on penalties after 1-1 draw
2. Arsenal beat Chelsea on penalties after 1-1 draw

3. Arsenal beat Chelsea 1-0
4. Arsenal beat Manchester City 3-0
5. Arsenal beat Manchester United 3-1
6. Arsenal beat Liverpool 1-0
7. Arsenal beat Manchester United 2-1
8. Arsenal beat Manchester United 3-0
9. Arsenal shared the trophy with Tottenham after 0-0 draw
10. Arsenal beat Blackpool 3-1. Stanley Matthews playing for Blackpool was given man of the match even though he was on losing side

QUIZ: 50 MISCELLANEOUS ANSWERS

1. It was Piazzagate as Fabregas allegedly threw pizza at the opposition
2. Real Madrid
3. It was Emmanuel Adebayor
4. Lyon
5. Stewart Houston
6. It was Thierry Henry
7. They wore Nike shirts
8. And were sponsored by O2
9. The trophy was gold
10. It was the first game to be broadcast live on the radio
11. Arsenal had 7 players in the England team
12. It was Phillipe Senderos
13. Norwich City
14. He scored 178 goals
15. £25 million
16. 1915 was the last time they were in the second tier
17. Divos Mavropanos made 3 appearances and managed to get a red card
18. Danny Welbeck joined the club
19. It was Cheryl
20. New training ground opened in Shenley in 1999
21. It was held at the Stade de France

22. Edu became the club's first technical director
23. He is a director
24. He is Czech
25. Arsenal have won 82, Tottenham 65 and 54 draws
26. Manchester United
27. Blackburn Rovers
28. United's lead over Arsenal was 18 points
29. He was from Yorkshire
30. It was about Alan Ball
31. He made 300 appearances
32. He scored 7
33. They have done it 3 times 1970-71, 1997-98 and 2001-02
34. It was the first match to be shown in 3D
35. He is Austrian
36. Chelsea
37. Score was 4-1
38. It was held in Azerbaijan
39. Sylvain Wiltord
40. Andy Ducat – Denis Compton didn't play football for England
41. Patrick Vieira 8 times
42. Atletico Madrid
43. He was a full back
44. Emmanuel Petit
45. 584 appearances
46. He is Chilian
47. It was George Eastham
48. Peter was an 11 year old when he won a contest with his design of Gunnersaurus
49. They've won 14 FA Cups
50. They are Jens Lehman(38), Thierry Henry(37), Kolo Toure(36), Sol Campbell(35), Robert Pires(33), Ashley Cole(32), Lauren(30), Patrick Vieira(29), Gilberto Silva(29), Freddie Ljungberg(27) and Dennis Bergkamp(21). A very useful team.

QUOTATIONS ANSWERS

1. Arsene Wenger on Mourinho calling him a voyeur
2. Charlie Nicholas
3. Arsene Wenger
4. Arsene Wenger
5. Charlie George
6. Arsene Wenger
7. Harry Kane
8. Dennis Bergkamp
9. Mesut Ozil
10. Robin van Persie
11. Paul Merson
12. Brian Marwood
13. Ian Wright
14. Graham Taylor
15. Arsene Wenger
16. Nicolas Anelka
17. Ian Wright
18. Theo Walcott
19. Ian Wright, on Tony Adam's confession to alcoholism
20. Charlie Nicholas
21. Ian Wright
22. Paul Merson
23. Emmanuel Adebayor
24. Niall Quinn
25. Prince Philip on seeing an Arsenal sponsor's logo
26. Ian Wright
27. Arsene Wenger on Thierry Henry's retirement
28. Tony Adams
29. Arsene Wenger on Robert Pires
30. George Graham
31. Arsene Wenger
32. Steve Bould
33. David O'Leary
34. Brian Clough
35. Arsene Wenger in 2002
36. Arsene Wenger
37. David O'Leary

38. Tony Adams
39. Sol Campbell
40. Thierry Henry
41. John Hollins
42. Bruce Rioch
43. Lee Dixon
44. Lee Dixon
45. Alan Ball
46. Nasser Hussein
47. Frank McLintock
48. Lee Dixon
49. Kenny Sansom
50. George Allison

ONE LAST THING…

If you have enjoyed this book I would love you to write a review of the book on Amazon. It is really useful feedback as well as giving untold encouragement to the author.

If you have any comments, corrections, suggestions for improvements or for other books I would love to hear from you, and you can contact me at;

jamesconradbooks@gmail.com

Your comments are greatly valued, and the books have already been revised and improved as a result of helpful suggestions from readers.

Printed in Great Britain
by Amazon

18233666R00058